A ROYAL CROWNING ACHIEVEMENT

KEVIN DWARES

A Royal Crowning Achievement

Visit our website at
www.StillwaterPress.com
for more information.

First Stillwater River Publications Edition

ISBN: 978-1-958217-97-9

Names: Dwares, Kevin, author.
Title: A royal crowning achievement / Kevin Dwares.
Description: First Stillwater River Publications edition. | Paw-
    tucket, RI, USA : Stillwater River Publications, [2023]
Identifiers: ISBN: 978-1-958217-97-9
Subjects: LCSH: Dwares, Kevin--Health. | Dentistry--Humor. |
    Teeth--Care and hygiene--Humor. | LCGFT: Autobiographies.
    | Humor.
Classification: LCC: PN6231.D4 D93 2023 | DDC:
    617.600207--dc23

1 2 3 4 5 6 7 8 9 10
Written by Kevin Dwares.
Cover and interior design by Elisha Gillette.

Published by Stillwater River Publications,
Pawtucket, RI, USA.

Dedicated to my granddaughter Maya Dwares

A Royal Crowning Achievement stars tooth number 18
with a supporting cast of characters: teeth numbers
19, 31, 30, 23, 24, 25, 26, 2, 3, 7, 8, 9, and 10.

The "toothful" story of two-plus years' worth
of appointments with my dentist!

TABLE OF CONTENTS

DEDICATION

This book is dedicated to my loving, funny, and intelligent granddaughter Maya who for the last two years (between the ages of nine and eleven) always asked me how I felt, and if I was okay while my dental work was getting done. She did get rather annoyed at me when every time she came over for a visit or when we Zoomed, I asked her if she wanted to see my teeth. At first she laughed about it but as time went on she got a little frustrated with me and asked me to stop. I tried to stop asking her but it became a ritual that she had to endure. I did promise her that the day that I finally had my last four crowns cemented on I would never again ask her if she wanted to see my teeth. I hope I can live up to this commitment.

Maya has a great passion for animals and tells me that she may want to become a veterinarian. Maya is also a very loyal and trustworthy friend, especially when it comes to her close circle of schoolmates.

She always knows when to hug me or give me a quick zinger of a joke to cheer me up. I am very lucky and grateful that she is my one and only (and favorite) grandchild and I will always love her.

For Maya's patience and love and good-natured ribbing of me I dedicate this book to her. Hopefully when she decides to read it she will realize that I was only joking with her about my teeth even though she sometimes was annoyed with me.

I love you Maya and I always will,
Papa

PREFACE

Beginning on June 29, 2020 and continuing through October 31, 2022, the author had fourteen dental crowns inserted and underwent many other dental procedures like bonding, fillings, and the reshaping of teeth. Mostly they were related to years of grinding down my teeth due to a dental condition called "bruxism."

What is bruxism you may ask? "Bruxism" is the involuntary habitual grinding of the teeth, typically during sleep. This is generally caused by stress and anxiety. This can also be caused by jaw problems, intense concentration, or anxiety. This condition can affect adults and children. Think about the evil monster, or dragon, or giant ape. They usually show their teeth with a lot of noise and grinding. I wouldn't say I relate to an ape even though some scholars do say that humans have evolved from these creatures. If this issue isn't addressed in time you may need a dental crown. The crown you can envision is usually worn by a king or queen, but I am referring to what goes over a tooth to protect it when the tooth you were born with is affected by wear and tear.

I decided to keep notes and a journal of my teeth issues since I knew that someday my teeth problems would come back to bite me over and over (no pun intended). You will see when you continue reading my story that I may have a strange sense of humor but I feel that it is always good to speak from the heart and tell the tooth and nothing but the tooth.

Why in the world would I want to write a book about two-plus years of dental appointments dealing with misery related to dental problems? Wouldn't it have been better to not air out dirty laundry in public and keep medical and dental issues to myself? I thought about this the entire time that I wrote my book.

Many friends and relatives told me that I should simply "grin and bear it" and just deal with it. However, I have in the past been the type of individual who would keep emotions in check and keep everything inside. I have decided this time that it will be very cathartic to write down my story, as told by me, typed by me, and most importantly experienced by me. I thought while writing that perhaps more people should put pen to paper to experience emotions and let the stress dissipate through words. I only say these things since writing this short true story did indeed help me to get some of the stress out, and I must admit; it felt good to do so. It's your life and your call whether to keep everything bottled up inside or to release your emotions by taking pen to paper as I have done.

I have always been the type of individual to keep meticulous records of everything; receipts of items I have purchased over $25.00 including warranty paperwork, and all of my medical and dental records and bills and payments. While I thought about writing a book about my experience, I actually began by keeping a small handwritten journal based upon my records. So after deciding it was time to put pen to paper, I put together my records and notebooks from the last two years and began on May 9, 2022.

Originally I had a few names for this book. They ranged from, "The Tooth is Out There" (this was ruled out since I thought it sounded too much like a science fiction novel), to "The Tooth Will Set You Free" (ruled out for reasons too numerous to mention), to "Grin and Bear It: Flash Those Pearly Whites," and "Do You Want to See My Teeth?". I had to rule out that last one since every time I said that to my granddaughter Maya, she said, "Oh Papa, stop it." I finally settled on the actual title of my book, *A Royal Crowning Achievement*, which in plain and everyday language means "Life sometimes sends you a curveball. It's how you bite back that counts." I therefore decided that my two-plus years' journey was a great accomplishment for me. Talking and writing about it actually made me feel better and realize that the last two years were not wasted but actually a great and long lasting "achievement," hence the name of my book.

Over the last sixty-five plus years of my life, I hated going to the dentist even though for a majority of that time I was a patient of two of my late uncle's dental practices. I guess I can't argue too much since I never had to pay a bill, make an appointment well in advance, or deal with any insurance companies. So in reality I had no pain with never taking out my credit card or filling out loads of ridiculous insurance paperwork relating to a dental claim. Like most of you the only real pain was the time spent sitting in the dental chair getting novocaine shots and the occasional drilling of my teeth. I guess in that regard I could be considered lucky.

This luck lasted for me from the day of my birth on October 28, 1955 until June 29, 2020, a span of nearly sixty-five years. I didn't spend nearly that kind of time in a dental chair but the two years plus that I did, from June 29, 2020 to October 31, 2022, seemed like an eternity.

A lot of people have asked me how it is possible that I had nearly forty-plus appointments during this time frame and I tell them that dental issues that either happen on their own or are created by someone else can take a lot of time, money, and effort to rectify. In hindsight I should have taken my teeth grinding issue much more seriously when I was in my teen years; then perhaps I wouldn't have had this many dental issues and wouldn't be writing this. I implore the reader: don't wait until the later years of your life to take your dental care seriously like I did.

Beginning in the next few pages I will tell you my saga, and it will be nothing but the tooth. Some of my friends laughed when I told them I was writing a book about dental issues. They said that serious medical issues like cancer, heart transplants, kidney dialysis, and similar diseases are real concerns and that while dental issues do occur, they are not in the same league. I agree, but the point is not to downplay cancer or say that dental problems are any more or less serious; it's my own personal reflection on what I had to resolve with my teeth over the last two-plus years. No more and no less.

Many people have teeth issues and don't ever address them for various reasons, such as shame, cost, time, and what I believe is the most important one: FEAR. I thought that telling my story as factually as I can, with a little sense of humor, might help someone else who can't deal with the stress of all the dental work that I myself had to endure. I won't sugarcoat my story but will add some humor and levity to put the reader at ease (for example, my tale begins when my dog Harry decided to eat the night guard my dentist prescribed!).

My story focuses mainly on tooth number 18, but many other teeth were affected along the way. Everything here is 100 percent the tooth, the whole tooth, and nothing but the tooth, so help me G-d.

You may wonder why I spell the word G-d instead of the most common spelling with three letters. Throughout my life I have always spelled the name G-d out of my own personal belief and respect. Some people of the Jewish faith believe that this is a sign of respect and comes from an interpretation of the commandment in Deuteronomy 12:4 regarding erasing, destroying, or desecrating the name of G-d. Writing "G-d" instead of spelling out the three letters is a fairly recent custom in America. According to the medieval commentator, Rashi, we should not erase or destroy G-d's name and should avoid writing it. Some people of the Jewish faith will avoid discarding paper or books in which G-d's name appears in Hebrew. Rather than being thrown out or destroyed, they may be stored in a *genizah* (a storage place) and buried in a Jewish cemetery.

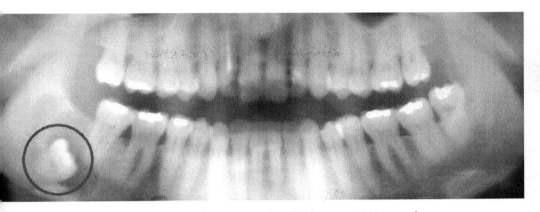

Actual panoramic photo of Kevin Dwares's teeth taken Oct. 2, 2020 at oral surgeon's office. The tooth circled in red (number 18) is the one that caused me all of the problems and the next two-plus years of appointments. I hated him at the time but luckily he still resides in my mouth, now much healthier.

During the time I wrote this book, I relied on my memory and thorough and meticulous records to be as accurate as possible. All of the events listed and detailed here are true. All of the appointment dates and procedure costs are factual and the author has supporting documentation in the form of calendars, notebooks, and Blue Cross Dental statements. No names, dental practices, or medical professionals are listed here. I simply used the terms general dentist, interim dentist, endodontist, periodontist, oral surgeon, dental hygienist, dental manager, and supporting staff.

The visits to numerous dental professionals actually all occurred during the period of June 29, 2020 through October 17, 2022 when my last four crowns were permanently cemented on. My final appointment was Monday, October 31, 2022 (Halloween) when the general dentist checked all of my fourteen dental crowns and told me that the mission was finally complete.

Now sit back, relax, and buckle in as you begin the ride of my lifetime and see how I descended through hell and back in what I like to call "The Dental Zone".

A respectful mention: During the last two-plus years while I was undergoing dental work, many people died from Covid. Close to six million died worldwide, over one million of them in the US. Although I personally endured two-plus years of pain and suffering, nothing compares to what went on during the pandemic.

A ROYAL
CROWNING
ACHIEVEMENT

WHY
"A ROYAL CROWNING
ACHIEVEMENT"?

While many people deal with numerous health issues over the years, some serious, some routine, and some ordinary, most people keep their health issues to themselves. I dealt with numerous teeth issues the last few years, during the pandemic. And I thought I would share that story with you so you have a few laughs and make light of things and realize life is too serious, silly, and boring at times. To tell the truth I hope you like my true tooth story. I could have put the blame for some of my dental issues on some of the dental professionals; instead I have decided to tell the tooth-full story and accept 100 percent of the responsibility. The thirty-two teeth in my mouth are mine and only mine and I am responsible for the maintenance, function, care, and control of them.

While some of the actual story and dates may appear disjointed at times this is due to the fact that during dental visits over the last two-plus years for specific teeth issues, each and every time I had an appointment inevitably other teeth issues arose that needed to be addressed. All of the appointment dates and procedures are fully documented by Blue Cross Dental insurance statements, along with dental notes, x-rays and charts, bills and payments, and are all in my possession. However, I first I need to give you a brief history of teeth, and their function and purpose.

TEETH: Human teeth function mainly to break down items of food by cutting and crushing them in preparation for swallowing and digesting. Humans have four types of teeth: incisors, canines, premolars, and molars. Each of these types has a specific function.

Why do humans need teeth? Every time we talk, smile and frown, and begin the process of digestion we use our mouths and our teeth. Our teeth let us make different facial expressions and form words—believe it or not the mouth is essential for speech.

THE BEGINNING OF THE JOURNEY

I usually don't post anything personal on Facebook, Nextdoor, or any other social publication, but thought some of my friends, neighbors, and acquaintances might find my saga interesting. Many of us mere mortals have experienced various types of medical issues and many have horror stories to relate about their experiences in the dental chair. During the unprecedented times we are all living in during the prevalence of Covid, a little humor at least one tooth at a time can go a long way. So here I begin to tell the tooth and nothing but the tooth of my personal dental journey from June 29, 2020 through October 31, 2022.

To begin my brief story, I will tell you first of all that both of my uncles (now both deceased) were dentists and always spoke to me of the importance of brushing and flossing after every meal. I was blessed with always having great teeth growing up. My parents (now both deceased) always stressed the importance of taking care of our teeth. From as early as nine or so years old I went to one of my two uncles for regular dental checkups and twice a year for a teeth cleaning. I can recall one year when I was about twelve years old when I had to visit Uncle Joe to have a small cavity taken care of. I was informed that if I didn't take care of the small cavity it would eventually bloom into a major issue. I learned at that visit that a major dental issue would require numerous novocaine shots and a lot of drilling. Of course I didn't pay that much attention to the advice and continued to eat fireballs and black licorice (two of my favorite snack foods) as often as possible. After my first experience with novocaine I vowed if at all possible to never have a very sharp needle jammed into my mouth ever again. I decided then and there to take care of my teeth and if I ever needed a cavity taken care of I would hold tightly onto the chair, forgo the needle, and take the pain like a man. In reality I wasn't a man but an idiot to take the pain, but I vowed to take care of my teeth to the best of my abilities.

Over the next many years, from age ten or so until age sixty or a span of half a century to the best of my recollection, I had few visits to the dentist except for regular teeth cleanings and the occasional filling taken care of (all without the dreaded needle) which I despised and to be honest I was afraid of. I did the best that I could to take care of my teeth except for the occasional stupid stunts that I liked to pull. One of these stunts (at age twelve and a half) involved me betting a good friend of mine that I could put three walnuts (complete with the shells) in my mouth and open all three of them. If I could manage this stunt I would earn ten bucks and an all-expenses-paid dinner at the local ice cream parlor. Well as you can imagine I did win the bet but spent the next day in my uncle's dental office having pieces of walnut shells pulled out of my gums. Suffice to say it was a very unpleasant visit. I don't know what was worse, my uncle yelling at me and telling me that it was time for me to grow up or having him tell me how much time he needed to spend on my mouth when he could have charged another patient a lot of money for serious dental work. He told me that if I ever came to see him again to have walnuts or any similar objects removed from the inside of my mouth, he would have to give me a bill and expect me to pay. I never returned to any dentist again for this type of dumb stunt.

My story begins with tooth number 18 which is called the second molar and is located on the bottom left side of my jaw. I will first tell you that I almost had to have my old friend, tooth number 18, extracted. He had been with me on many occasions, both joyful and sad. He always knew when to bite down lightly or tread with a heavy tooth, so to speak; how to chew the fat and bite when needed. He also knew when to grin and bear it, but always smiled when chatting with friends. I would have missed him if he came home in pieces.

I was always told to tell the tooth and nothing but the tooth, so here it goes.

Regarding tooth number 18, also known as the lower back molar or referred to in the dental world as the second molar, let me now get to the root of the story.

I had not seen my dentist since the Covid-19 outbreak which began during the month of March in 2020. Besides not seeing the dentist or any other medical professionals, all was well in the life, body, and mind of the author (me), that is until the fateful night of June 29, 2020. For most of you readers that day is just another date on the calendar. To me however, it is the day I got married to my sweetheart and my wife Barbara Gold Dwares on June 29, 1980, forty-plus years ago. Can you imagine, forty-plus years being married to someone who loves and cares for you? Living with me isn't always easy since I have some idiosyncrasies like most everyone else (but I am still close to perfection at least in my own mind).

On that Monday night over two-plus years ago my wife and I celebrated our fortieth wedding anniversary with some takeout from a local restaurant. We wanted to go to a nice restaurant to celebrate this most joyous occasion but due to Covid most places were closed.

We first decided to begin our special day with a visit to the location of our marriage forty years ago. We drove to the Praise Tabernacle Church on Park Ave. in Cranston, Rhode Island located across from Roger Williams Park. Our old Temple Torat Yisrael was formerly located here but has long since moved to East Greenwich, Rhode Island. We drove up and walked the exact route from the parking lot to the front of the building and took a few snapshots with our camera of what we looked like forty years after our wedding day. While outside a young lady came up to me and asked what we were doing. When I responded that our wedding took place here forty years back she stated that her dad was the current pastor of the church and she graciously invited us in to walk around the old temple. We walked into the main sanctuary and both thought back to our wedding day a long time ago. We had a lot of good and some not so good times since then. We thanked the pastor and his daughter and left reminiscing about our lives.

We then decided to go and have dinner (believe it or not) at a Newport Creamery in Garden City since we knew they had outdoor tables located in the parking lot. Unfortunately, when we arrived it started to rain quite heavily, and we were told that no outside dining would be possible.

After leaving the parking lot we ordered Chinese takeout. I can't remember the exact place, but I am sure we enjoyed taking a short drive just to get out of the house for an hour or so. We enjoyed a simple wedding anniversary dinner at home that evening. I was lucky that day in more ways than one, not just celebrating our longtime marriage but also enjoying our Chinese food and each other's company. We laughed about not being able to sit outside due to the weather but promised each other we would on our next anniversary (which, in fact, we did).

Later that night I began my nighttime ritual of brushing and flossing my teeth, taking my medication for cholesterol, and then preparing to go to sleep. If I recall it was around ten thirty, the usual time I try to begin my nightly routine. Upon reaching on top of my headboard to get my mouth guard, which is usually safe in the protective case, I immediately sensed a serious problem when I felt thick pieces of plastic. My night guard wasn't intact and instead was part of a leftover treat for our dog Harry. I immediately called Harry to come into my bedroom and he hung his head as if to feign sorrow for his actions. He couldn't speak any English that I could possibly decipher but I'm sure he must have been thinking the following phrases:

Kevin, you're the jackass who left the night guard out of its resting place. You and only you are responsible for its destruction. Don't blame me when apparently you are the idiot.

Harry immediately went to his best friend and confidant (Barbara) and after looking at him then her I realized that I couldn't win the battle, so I simply said I would contact the dental office the next morning.

In reality I was very mad and if I could have played Dr. Kevorkian for at least one brief moment, Harry the Dog would have endured...let's end my thoughts about this incident here while I am still standing tall and breathing....

I called the dentist the next day and made an appointment for him to look at my teeth and my night guard on Tuesday, June 30, 2020. The general dentist was a man of great humility with compassion for his patients. He always treated me with kindness and respect and also sought to make me comfortable in the dental chair. He knew that I didn't ever enjoy coming to the dentist, but I knew I needed to come in for an appointment. We would always chat about current events, world politics, the military, and the environment. I was sorry to see him retire in the fall of 2020.

On that visit the general dentist took x-rays of all of my teeth

Top: *Picture of Harry the Dog*
Left: *Picture of Harry the Dog and his trusty sidekick Sally the Cat*

to make sure that nothing major had changed since my last visit. Dental impressions were taken of my mouth so a new night guard could be made. During that visit the dentist also bonded a small chip in tooth number 27, which is located in the bottom of the jaw. He also noticed a few small fractures in teeth numbers 18, 30, and 31 located in the bottom jaw, probably related to me grinding my teeth. They needed to be crowned as soon as possible. I made that appointment for Monday, July 6, 2020. I also made an appointment for Friday, August 14, 2020 to begin the crown preparation for tooth number 18.

My dentist had discussed with me many times how the frequent grinding of teeth, if not addressed properly, will come back to bite you (no pun intended). Most likely due to me grinding my teeth for most of my adult life and not always wearing my night guard, I was informed that sometime in the near future, I would need fourteen to sixteen crowns. When I asked why I was told that due to my heavy teeth grinding over the years, many of my teeth had small fractures in them and these issues needed to be addressed in the immediate future. I always put this off, but after the night guard being used by my dog Harry as an after-dinner snack, the time had come for my teeth to be crowned. At this stage I agreed with the dentist that, for the sake of my teeth, I would have the many crowns (twelve to fourteen of them) put on in the next year or so.

On Monday, July 6, 2020 I once again had a dental appointment and began the process of having teeth numbers 30 and 31 drilled and shaped for new crowns. While this process may seem simple to some patients, for me it was extremely painful and torturous since I never did well with novocaine. Every time I got the needle I would immediately get queasy and develop a terrible headache. The response I got was the drilling would only take a few minutes and I would need to grin and bear the pain as it would improve my teeth, their functions, and my overall dental health (what a bunch of malarkey). Pain is pain and I have nothing else to say about it.

On Monday, July 20, 2020 I returned to the office to have the two new crowns permanently cemented on for teeth numbers 31 and 30, which at that point I thought would be the end of my journey. That was far from the tooth. This would begin more than a two-year journey which almost allowed me to become an honorary member of the American Dental Association, at least in my own mind. I learned more than anyone would care to about the inner workings of a dental office. I also learned almost every minute detail of the mouth, the positioning of each tooth, and the function and purpose of each. It was a quite an experience, one which I would love to forget.

Less than two weeks later, on Tuesday, August 4, 2020 I contacted the dental office to complain that tooth number 18 was hurting and they told me to come into the office for x-rays. At the same time the dentist said that I should have my teeth cleaned by the dental hygienist to have any decay or tartar that had built up around the teeth removed. Lucky for me they scheduled that dental hygienist appointment for that afternoon. During this visit the general dentist noticed that tooth number 18 located on the lower jaw, had a severe fracture most likely from not wearing a night guard the last few weeks. Fortunately I'd already made another dental appointment for Friday, August 14, 2020 to begin preparation for a crown for tooth number 18 during my June 30 visit.

Since I had two crowns installed a few weeks before the August 14 appointment, when it rolled around I had an idea as to the procedure of preparing a tooth for a new crown.

Before the process of making a crown begins, your dentist will anesthetize (numb) the tooth and the gum tissue around the tooth. Next, the tooth receiving the crown is reshaped along the chewing surface and sides to make room for the crown. The amount removed depends on the type of crown used; suffice to say, after getting a novocaine shot, the dentist drills the tooth down to a new shape so that the new technologically designed tooth can fit over the original tooth's surface.

I was told at that appointment that the new permanent crown would arrive in the next few weeks, so long as the laboratories were working with a full staff, what with Covid running rampant. By this time, I was getting slightly frustrated as every time I had discussions with my dentist and his staff, the term Covid always reared its ugly head in relation to my appointments and dental work.

Sometime after my appointment on Friday, August 14, 2020 I was contacted by the secretary in my general dentist's office and was told the dentist would be retiring and an interim one would be hired during the process of the dental practice being purchased. I wasn't too concerned about this since it was and is always my assumption that dental professionals are highly educated and experienced in their field of study.

The dental office manager also contacted me to let me know that the new, permanent crown for number 18 would be in the office on Monday, September 14, 2020, so I scheduled an appointment for that day to have it cemented in place. I met the new interim dentist that day and she went over both my medical and dental history since, being new, she needed to know me as well as my past and potential dental issues.

During that visit the dentist indicated to me that tooth number 19 (bottom jaw) also had a fracture in it due to my teeth grinding and also would need a crown in the not too distant future. I scheduled an appointment for number 19 crown preparation for Monday October 5, 2020.

Following my original dentist's advice, I began what I thought would be an easy process. As you read on, you will realize nothing was further from the tooth.

On Monday, September 14, 2020 I had the permanent crown for tooth number 18 inserted by the interim dentist. While the dentist was putting on the new crown prior to it being permanently cemented in place, I told her that the tooth below the surface was painful and the new crown wasn't fitting properly. I was told that the pain from below the surface of the tooth is generally caused by prior decay in the tooth and all of the grinding and drilling to prepare its surface for the new crown. However, I insisted that the tooth hurt. However, I was told that I would get used to the new crown and that the pain would subside in a few days at most. I left the interim dentist with the new crown on number 18 feeling very uncomfortable, even though I repeatedly told her that the crown was too high, was not fitting properly, and causing extreme pain below the surface of my gum.

After the crown was inserted for tooth number 18 on Monday, September 14, 2020, I began to experience an enormous amount of pain in my mouth, had a very severe headache, and swollen and inflamed gums. On Friday, September 18, 2020 I contacted the interim dentist and told her that my mouth was inflamed and I was in extreme pain. At this stage I was prescribed 800 mg of ibuprofen to help with the mouth pain. I was told to call the dentist back over the weekend if the pain didn't subside. On Saturday, September 19, 2020 I called the dentist again complaining that my mouth was inflamed and I had sores all around the gum near tooth number 18. This time at my insistence the dentist prescribed azithromycin just in case I had some type of dental infection (which later on was determined to be accurate). My mouth didn't seem to get any better and the pain didn't subside. On Monday, September 21, 2020 I contacted the dentist again and was told to come into the office immediately (which of course I did). The dentist seemed to be slightly annoyed with me, but I protested that there had to be some reason for all of my pain. I was told that I needed to give the pain medication more time to work and I then insisted that I needed an appointment with another type of dental professional. Even though the interim dentist told me that it would take time for my tooth to settle down with the new crown, the dentist contacted a local endodontist (specializes in root canal procedure) to schedule an appointment for Tuesday, September 22, 2020. They'd look at my tooth and make a determination if a root canal was possibly needed.

At my appointment with the endodontist, numerous x-rays were taken of my mouth focusing on tooth number 18 and its new crown, which at this point had been hurting me for a week. The examination revealed that I did indeed need a root canal and it could be done immediately or in two future appointments. I chose to grin and bear it and I had three novocaine shots before the drilling began. This procedure required drilling right through the brand new crown. After the pain and suffering concluded, I was given a temporary filling in the new crown and was referred back to the interim dentist to have a permanent filling put in tooth number 18.

I did ask the endodontist why it wasn't determined that I needed a root canal prior to having tooth number 18 crowned and was told simply that sometimes the root structure below the gum-line can get inflamed and infected due to the drilling of a tooth for crown preparation. I took her at her word and decided she had told me nothing but the tooth.

A few days after the root canal procedure I once again began to have extreme pain and very sore gums. The endodontist referred me to a periodontist for a Friday, October 2, 2020 visit to have my gums examined.

I met the periodontist, whose job specializes in health of gums and jawbones, and felt extremely comfortable with him as he began to perform an oral examination of my mouth. The examination revealed that my gums were very sore and painful but at this time the tooth would need time to heal. I was extremely nervous, especially when I saw a tray table filled with needles, pliers, and other tools of the trade (Was I in a dental office or a torture chamber?).

I jokingly asked the dentist if he smelled Chinese food and he asked me if I felt okay since that was an odd comment. I told him that the local Jewish funeral home across the street used to be a Chinese restaurant. It also was the location of my twenty-year-old son Max's funeral on Thursday, February 19, 2004. I told the periodontist that my son passed away the day before his funeral from complications relating to a bone marrow transplant to cure him of chronic myelogenous leukemia. The dentist remembered all of the social media surrounding my son when we were trying to find him a bone marrow donor match.

The periodontist then referred me to an oral surgeon who was supposed to examine my tooth for evaluation. Luckily for me he was able to schedule me an appointment with the oral surgeon that same day, Friday, October 2, 2020.

During the initial visit to the oral surgeon a panoramic x-ray (Appendix B) was taken of my entire mouth which revealed numerous fractures and a potential issue with number 18's crown. The oral surgeon prescribed a course of antibiotics and told me that if the inflammation coming from that area didn't resolve itself, the tooth would have to be extracted in the next few weeks. He did, however, tell me that I should have the permanent crown for tooth number 19 cemented on as soon as possible since a temporary crown can lead to bacteria and germs getting under the gums, which could cause more issues in the immediate future. Before leaving I made a follow-up with the oral surgeon to have him reexamine my tooth and determine if it might need to be extracted.

On Monday, October 5, 2020 I once again returned to the interim dentist to begin preparing tooth number 19 for a permanent crown. Since by this time I knew the pain and suffering that would ensue, I prophylactically took 800 mg of ibuprofen to hopefully ward off or at least lessen the bad headache that normally occurred when I had dental pain. I made an appointment to have the permanent crown cemented in for Thursday, October 22, 2020.

On Thursday, October 8, 2020 I returned to the oral surgeon with a very bad feeling in my gut. I anticipated him informing me that tooth number 18 would have to be extracted. However, the oral surgeon told me that he thought the antibiotics were helping with my infection and decided I should try another dose and come back on October 20 for a reevaluation. I was informed that sometimes after a crown procedure bacteria can escape from the pulp of the tooth, which can necessitate a root canal, which can then cause further tooth breakdown and massive gum infection. On occasion a root canal can fail. After I heard him say that, my stomach was in knots.

After numerous dental appointments in the last three weeks for tooth pain, including thirteen shots of novocaine, two prescriptions of Z-pak, and two for amoxicillin, I was hopefully soon to be pain free.

All of this of course was very expensive with a few thousand dollars in out-of-pocket costs, and a lot of time in various dental establishments. I guess the only thing I will be getting from the tooth fairy is a Visa bill.

I told the oral surgeon to tell me the tooth and nothing but the tooth. I probably should have seen a witch doctor instead. I have always had good teeth. I brush and floss after every meal. I don't smoke or drink but was thinking I might pick up this bad habit after the past few weeks. At least my tooth was finally at peace since at least for the time being it was not in pieces. Tooth be told, this is *almost* the final update on tooth number 18. As usual I promise to tell the tooth and nothing but the tooth.

Tuesday, October 20 in the year 2020 at 7:55 a.m. A day that will last in infamy, at least for number 18.

I ascended the stairs on the way to my oral surgeon's office located in Cranston, Rhode Island, where he would make a final decision as to the status of my tooth in the next few minutes.

As I climbed each and every step my heart was pounding, my hands were sweaty and shaky and my mind began to wander. I became nervous and fearful at what might next be happening to me and tooth number 18.

I think I could actually feel what it may be like when a prisoner takes his final steps towards the execution chamber, or when a gladiator from days past was about to enter the ring to fight for his life and death against an opponent.

I tried to calm myself down, told myself that I was not experiencing a life-and-death situation but simply a tooth possibly in peril and about to begin the journey home to the wastebasket in the dental office.

I thought of all the time I'd spent with number 18 over the last sixty-five years.

Tooth number 18 was born October 28, 1955 at the old Lying-Inn Hospital on Smith Street in Providence. He began his life in the mouth of a cute, curly haired baby appropriately named "Kevin," son of the late Robert Joseph Dwares and Shirley Bella Gold Dwares.

The name Kevin means "handsome." It has Irish roots and is derived from the name Caoimhín, which originated from the elements *coém* (meaning "handsome") and *gein* (meaning "birth"). Saint Kevin was the first well-known Kevin. Since then, many children have been given the name. I wasn't born a saint, never was considered a saint, and simply was referred to as Kevin from birth up to and including the date of the publication of my book.

To get back to the story of tooth number 18...

Tooth number 18 was a fairly light tooth weighing in at approximately 1.8 ounces. My mother was told that my tooth weighed more than the average tooth since it had four roots. Enough about the birth of my tooth.

I began to think of all the times dining with my tooth at local restaurants, eating chicken and asparagus, or breakfast like bacon and eggs, or cheeseburgers, and of course one of my favorite nutritious items with my favorite flavor: butter crunch ice cream.

There was a very real possibility that all these were going to end for number 18.

I approached the office door and took a deep breath. The receptionist took my temperature, blood pressure, and my oxygen level as required due to Covid-19 and I was very surprised when she told me all was fine. She then told me the oral surgeon would be seeing me shortly. That made as happy as anything.

I looked in the mirror on the wall and proudly gazed at my teeth, including number 18. Nostalgia set in. My stomach was in knots and I began to get nervous and felt the urge to get up and quickly leave the office. However, I realized that I would have to come back again so I decided to stay and await my fate. To tell you the tooth I was petrified, thinking of all the torture and pain and suffering I was about to experience

I realized that day would hopefully be my last visit to the oral surgeon so I intended to make a final good impression.

The dental assistant called my name, escorted me into the dental office, and asked how I was feeling. I wanted to tell her that I felt like crap; my head felt like it was in a vise and my stomach was dancing the Macarena at 33 RPM. However, I tried to be my usual good-natured self and simply said fine and I proceeded to ask her how her day was going.

I was escorted over to the chair and was told to sit down and recline if I chose while I waited for the oral surgeon to appear. I shut my eyes for a moment or two and awaited my fate.

Like a fool I glanced over to the small table next to me. It was covered by a small green cloth. I gently lifted up the cover and saw a few very shiny tools like pliers, metal picks, a very sharp knife and a screwdriver (which looked like they were just purchased from my local hardware store) and of course the usual rather large hypodermic needle filled with novocaine.

I wasn't sure if I was in the dentist's office or the office of Count Dracula and his loyal assistants Drs. Frank and Stein. My mind also began to drift and the first thing I thought about was the movie *Braveheart* that starred Mel Gibson as William Wallace, the medieval Scottish patriot who is spurred into revolt against the English when the love of his life is executed. Prior to William Wallace being put to death he was to undergo a brutal torture session with the same tools (although not as sterile) as those I envisioned the oral surgeon would be using on me shortly.

I took a big gulp of air and swallowed deeply when the surgeon pronounced, "Open wide, time to begin." Do you think I felt any better when he uttered those few words? Of course not, I actually thought I was going to begin vomiting all over, but took a deep breath and waited for the end to come.

The tooth would soon be upon me. The surgeon gazed into my mouth of pearly whites and with amazement announced "Your gums are 100 percent healed and no extraction is necessary." I leaped out of the chair and hugged the doctor and the dental assistants (socially distanced if course). It seemed I had a new lease at life with number 18. It was no longer going to be taken for granted. I would be able to live my last days on Earth with a full set of pearly whites including number 18. I would cherish life every day and never again take my teeth for granted and never bite off more than I could chew.

I cheerfully ran down the hallway and pumped my arms in the air like Sylvester Stallone did in *Rocky*. Alright, tooth be told I actually walked down the stairs and out into the fresh air. I did however (although not too loud so as not to embarrass myself) yell "Freedom!" as the torture session I had envisioned a few minutes ago never did materialize.

I won the battle but perhaps not the final war of the teeth as age can easily humble us all.

While I may have hoped to be done with all dentists for the near future, little did I realize that I would have many more appointments in the next few years.

MY FINAL THOUGHTS ON TOOTH NUMBER 18
(OR SO I THOUGHT)

We all know life is precious and I don't presume to preach to anyone, but at that very moment I decided quite simply that I intended to enjoy every moment of the rest of mine. Some of the readers may have begun to ask themselves "Why oh why is Kevin spending so much time talking about his damn teeth when there are so many more important issues to be concerned with?" My simple response would have to be this: Each and every one of us at some time has an issue that is important. It may be loss of a loved one, loss of a job, a disease like cancer or a medical issue that on the surface seems rather simple. And I of course agree. However, what the reader may not see from my story is all the pain and suffering my mouth had gone through, all the shots, appointments, stomachaches, headaches and more. Each of us deals with trauma in their own way.

As you can now realize I deal with tension and stress by talking about it, by making jokes and putting pen to paper. These are all cathartic to me and have served to allow me to express myself and my emotions. I used the same techniques after my son Max passed away at the age of twenty on February 18, 2004 from complications relating to his leukemia. That was an extremely stressful time for Max, myself, and my immediate family. I needed a way to vent my feelings. Out of that came my first published book entitled *Live to the Max*.

I also have decided that I can't and won't take a small bite of the apple of life; I will bite the entire thing. I will no longer complain about things I have no control over. If things get difficult I will just grin and bear it and move forward and always live life to the fullest. I will get up each and every day and be thankful for all that I have. Tooth be told, none of us can know the day or time the clock will stop on our existence. So as far as I go, I intend to not just take a bite of life, I will live my life to the Max and I hope you all do as well.

Online, many people have privately messaged me to ask why I sign off all the time by saying "Live to the Max" and *l'chaim*. The answer to their great significance to me has to do with my Jewish faith and my family.

The word *chaim* is the Hebrew word for "alive." *L'Chaim* in Hebrew is a toast meaning "to life." When a couple becomes engaged, they get together with friends and family to celebrate. Since they drink *l'chaim* ("to life"), the celebration is also called a *l'chaim*.

As for the other phrase, on February 18, 2004, at the age of twenty, my son Max passed away from complications related to his battle with leukemia. Max was a kind and gentle human being. He always believed in the goodness of mankind and through his faith and belief in G-d, he "lived life to the Max."

Max had begun writing a book about his experience but passed away shortly thereafter. It is called *Live to the Max*. To honor his memory, I worked on the book for twelve years till I finally had it published four years ago. The book is at the Cranston Public Library or can be purchased online at Amazon or Google. All proceeds go to the Tomorrow Fund of Hasbro Children's Hospital for children with cancer. If you happen to read the book, feel free to tell me your experiences in reading it. Thank you.

Be careful out there and enjoy. And finally always remember: The Tooth will set you Free and Live to the Max.

Wishing you good health and happiness in the years to come. *L'Chaim* (to life).

THE ALMOST, ALMOST
FINAL INSTALLMENT. HOPEFULLY

I thought after my appointment with the oral surgeon on Tuesday, October 20, 2020 that all of my dental issues were behind me. However, I began to notice an irritation on my gum directly adjacent to tooth number 18 a few days after that "final" visit. A canker sore was developing on my gum, or so I thought. I contacted the oral surgeon and he told me that canker sores and gum and mouth irritations can develop any time a lot of dental work is done. I was advised to keep an eye on the irritation and call back my dentist if it didn't get better. I was also told to have the permanent crown cemented on tooth number 19.

On Thursday, October 22, 2020 I went to the general dentist to have the permanent crown for number 19 inserted. I have little to say about this tooth, other than I didn't realize in a few short weeks my mouth would be in pain once again.

Along the way I had another appointment at my dental office with the dental hygienist on Monday, November 2, 2020 to have my teeth cleaned and also had a mold taken of my full set of teeth so I could be fitted for a new night guard. This appointment went fairly well and it was peaceful for a change. The only thing that I don't like about this procedure is that when the paste-filled tray is inserted in my mouth I generally gag and feel that I am choking to death. Thankfully this only lasted for a few minutes before I could escape the chair and the office.

Over the weekend I began to notice a sort of raised and quite sharp edge of what I thought was a canker sore. It irritated the side of my tongue when I rubbed it against the raised area of the presumed canker.

I put on some canker medicine but it didn't seem to help. As a matter of fact, the sore got more and more painful and actually felt hard like a small piece of a bone. On Monday, November 9, 2020 I called my dentist to make an appointment for that day. I was referred to my periodontist to look at what was bothering me (this time!).

I went to the periodontist that very morning and he looked at the offending area and concluded that it could be a piece of bone fragment that began to grow through the gum next to tooth number 18. The periodontist indicated it could have broken off below the gumline from either having the crown inserted, or more likely from the root canal.

The actual name of the bone is called a "lingual (no, not linguine) bone spur." The tooth of the matter is I couldn't wait to have the sliver of bone removed. The periodontist explained that I had nothing to worry about. He said that mouth bone spurs can develop after any type of oral tooth work and your body will automatically get rid of them (most of the time). If not, they have to be removed by a periodontist.

The next step involved an x-ray and then a small pair of tweezers inserted above the spur, and within a second or two the fragment was removed. The removal procedure tooth be told was painless.

Well, this concludes the story of tooth number 18 (for real this time!). It ended well and I still have one of my favorite pearly whites.

I told you the tooth and nothing but the tooth during my saga. I am sure that you all could handle the tooth.

MORE TEETH ISSUES

On November 23, 2020 I went back to the dentist to get my newly made night guard. The night guard appeared to be too tight and I told them in the office. The dental technician adjusted it and said I would get used to it as my teeth would adjust to the night guard in time. To be quite frank I felt very uncomfortable leaving the office but was told that the night guard would feel better after a few days' use. How wrong I was. Sitting in my car I thought that I should go back into the office and complain. However, since I already had so many appointments I didn't want to have my picture posted on the office wall as one of the top ten complainers. Instead I drove home and muttered to myself, and hoped for the best. Little did I know that same evening more dental woes would befall me.

The same evening, when I was putting the night guard in prior to going to sleep, the crown of tooth number 30, crowned on Monday, July 20, 2020, popped off. I was very angry, frustrated, and to be very honest, mad as hell. I called the general dentist and they made me an appointment to re-cement it on Tuesday, December 1, 2020 since that was the only time available. This wasn't my main dentist since he was away, and I was directed to a dentist in another practice that was part of my large dental group. I arrived at the dental office early in the morning with a chip on my shoulder (no pun intended) and informed the dentist what had happened. He explained in layman's terms that occasionally crowns can be pulled off by a night guard, similar to why your dentist tells you not to eat sticky candy. The dentist simply cleaned the area around my crown on tooth number 30, cemented it back into place, and said I was good for another hundred thousand miles, ten years, or whatever came first.

Meanwhile on Wednesday, December 9, 2020 I had another dental appointment to bond teeth numbers 8 and 9. The dentist indicated that due to my grinding and not having a night guard for almost 147 days (Monday, June 29, 2020 – Monday, November 23, 2020) and the issues with teeth numbers 18 and 19, my mouth was a mess. I was hoping against all odds that this would be my last dental appointment for some time, but this would not come to pass. Within nine short days I would be back.

This time on December 18, the crown of number 19 fell off while I was drinking water and eating a small piece of soft cheese. I called the dentist and they made me an appointment for the morning of Monday, December 21, 2020 to temporarily cement the crown back on. (see anecdote #1 when I met the new permanent dentist in the hallway)

After feeling very annoyed and aggravated (not my usual modus operandi) during that appointment, the general dentist who I really respect and always enjoy talking with said he would be contacting the owner of the dental group. He wanted the owner to speak to me about how they would rectify the numerous issues with my teeth and make me feel good about the world of dentistry again.

I was informed by the dental manager that the most senior dentist in the dental group would come to the office on Wednesday, December 30, 2020 to look at tooth number 19 to see if I needed a bone shaving so the crown would be properly fitted to the tooth. The dentist who would be taking over the dental practice was also present. This dentist went over both my medical and dental history since he was new to the practice and needed to know me as well as my dental history. The new dentist had an excellent manner about him. He was very friendly and highly educated with a great deal of dental experience. He immediately put my mind at ease and told me that he would take care of all of my teeth over the next few years. He answered every one of my questions and I trusted his decisions about my teeth 100 percent.

One of the dentists present indicated that he would never have put a crown on tooth number 19 due to the current condition of my teeth. I was also informed that nothing would be done with the night guard at this time since it wasn't the proper one for my teeth and a new one would not be made until all of the dental issues would be resolved.

During the conference with the dentists it was determined that the root of the problem (no pun intended) was the original place-ment of tooth number 18's crown, which might have not been put on correctly. It was also pointed out that I had a great deal of bruxism issues (grinding of teeth for those who forgot) and that the 147 days that I was without a new night guard exacerbated the dental problems.

I would like to point out the purpose of this book is to tell you a story of my teeth, NOT to place blame on anyone. I was told that if I had any additional issues with teeth numbers 18 and 19 they would have to be removed and replaced with new dental crowns.

Would you believe that further issues would once again develop with teeth in my mouth?

On Sunday, January 3, 2021 at 7:30 p.m., while at home drink-ing a glass of water, number 19's crown fell off again. I was livid and screaming and left numerous phone messages with the dental practice's answering service as well as with the regional manager for the dental group. When I finally received a call back from the on-call dentist I explained what had happened and I was told to come into the dental office on Monday, January 4, 2021 at 9:00 a.m. At this appointment a decision was made. Instead of having the crown re-cemented back, the crowns for 18 and 19 would be removed and the two teeth would be prepared for new crowns once again. An additional appointment was scheduled for Wednesday, January 6, 2021.

I arrived at the office to begin what would be a very painful experience, one that I will always remember but try to forget: the removal of the crowns on teeth numbers 18 and 19. I was imme-diately given numerous novocaine shots to numb the area where the two crowns would be removed. I glanced over and noticed that there were two dentists, a few dental technicians, and my wife all looking into the office to see if I was okay. The pain, while somewhat manageable at first, soon hurt like hell. As the lead dentist began pulling and yanking my head felt like it was going to explode. They poked, prodded, cut and yanked as if they were delivering an oversized baby calf out of his mom's birth canal.

The pain began to get more intense as the morning progressed. I could see that the spit bib around my neck was getting more and more wet and filled with the spit up, blood soaked crap that was drooling down my chin. I am not ashamed to admit that I needed to gasp for air a few times. Each time I asked how much longer this would take, the response was soon. Soon as in what the hell were they talking about? Soon as the executioner fired his shot, soon as the guillotine is dropped onto the intended victim's neck? Soon, soon, soon. At this stage all I felt was an uneaten two-pound lobster that was about to have its claw yanked, pinched, and broken off.

I decided to take a much needed break so I told the dentist to shut off the lights and leave me in my deep and dark tragic thoughts.

The dentists and technicians left the room and shut off the lights as I quickly drifted off to a much needed and restful sleep.

Five or ten minutes later I felt someone gingerly rubbing my shoulder and saying my name repeatedly, "Kevin, Kevin, Kevin." I was not responding as quickly as they thought I should. One of the medical professionals came within two inches of my face (socially distanced of course) with his mask on and whispered, "Are you okay?" To be honest, with all the pain I was in, I thought for a minute in my drug induced semicomatose state that I could grab him by the throat and strangle him, but I actually liked him so instead I began to doze off again. The other dentists told the dental assistant to get some smelling salts and be prepared to call 911 just in case. I could hear them chatting with my wife, and she told them I was deep sleeper and to just give it a few more minutes. At this point I asked myself if all of this pain and suffering was needed and reassured myself that dental issues develop through all stages of life and that I had some issues that need to be addressed. I continued to feign sleep and simply kept my eyes shut until I heard two dentists calling out my name and the concern in their voices when I didn't immediately respond. (See anecdote #2: playing dead in the chair.)

I could go much further into detail about the removal of crowns on teeth numbers 18 and 19 but to be quite frank with you, I am getting an upset stomach reliving this dental appointment.

I will leave the reader with this thought. I had to just continue with the dreaded ordeal, grin and bear it and to tell you the tooth, keep my mouth (metaphorically) shut, get the work finished, and get the hell out of the office. When I was ready to leave the dentist asked me how I felt and I responded simply "Like crap." I was exhausted, in pain, and felt like vomiting. I thought I would burst into tears, but wouldn't give the dentists and the office staff the satisfaction of seeing me that way. Instead I said nothing, I reached for my coat and walked to the door of the office and flung it open. I left the room like a wounded but conquering warrior or gladiator who successfully won his match but was too proud to admit pain and hurt. I could hear the dental manager say, "I have never seen Kevin so upset and mad. He has always been polite and a nice guy and patient." She knew to just let me leave and go home. That night and for a few days after I took pain medications to help my mouth heal. ENOUGH of this incident.

The new and improved permanent crowns for teeth 18 and 19 were cemented in on Tuesday, January 19, 2021. At this appointment the time flew by. No pain and suffering this time. Nothing more to say, except the dentist once again told me that I should address the other teeth that needed crowns. All of them. We chatted, I listened and I said maybe in the future. He said that he would for sure be seeing me in the future. I told him that since I had already had so many appointments, his office should introduce a rewards card for visits; the patient should get a free coupon for a local sub sandwich shop. He laughed and said no. I left the office and went home.

During the next year or so I had numerous dental appointments for various reasons, including cleaning and bonding of my lower and upper teeth. I also had ten additional crowns put in, these on teeth numbers 23-26, 2-3, and 7-10. I will briefly mention the type of work done for each tooth rather than bore the reader with all the details:

Monday, May 24, 2021: Tooth number 21 bonded after a small chip broke off.

Thursday, August 5, 2021: Teeth number 27 and 28 received fillings due to my grinding.

Wednesday, September 1, 2021: Number 24 got a filling.

Thursday, November 4, 2021: Number 25 got a filling and a bonded. After this appointment the dentist indicated that I should get teeth numbers 23-26 bonded as soon as I could.

Thursday, December 2, 2021: X-rays and oral exam of all teeth. At this visit I received my semiannual gift: a new toothbrush, a small container of dental floss, and a bill. Thank you to my dentist and all the staff.

On Monday December 13, 2021 work began on the preparation of my bottom four teeth, numbers 23-26, for crowns. Preparing a tooth for a crown is similar to cutting up a piece of steak with a very sharp knife. First of all, numerous shots of my favorite novocaine are administered and after a few minutes the mouth and the areas around the teeth to be worked on go numb. In case you're interested, I began to drool like an infant and spit out phlegm and blood and probably some guts. Since I already had teeth worked on for crowns this procedure, while painful, was nothing that I wasn't completely aware of. I shut my eyes and tried to drift off, but would open them occasionally and see the dentist with a dental drill in his hand and I felt some pain all over. By this time the dentist and I were friends and I no longer called him "The

Executioner" at least not to his face. Boy was I overjoyed when I left the office that day since I knew there would be no more pain and suffering for my teeth, at least not for a few weeks or so.

My next visit to my general dentist was on Monday, December 20, 2021 to have the four new dental crowns cemented on permanently for teeth numbers 23-26. However, the dentist wasn't happy with the fit of the crowns so he was only able to put on two of them, on teeth numbers 25 and 26, and send back to the laboratory for crowns for teeth 23 and 24. Putting on the new crowns this time was an easy and painless procedure.

On Thursday, January 20, 2022 I returned once again to one of my favorite places and had crowns for teeth numbers 23 and 24 cemented in place permanently with no complications. On the same visit, the general dentist bonded teeth numbers 2 and 3 due to small cracks in them, all attributed to me grinding my teeth due to bruxism. I was advised that in the not too distant future I had to have these two teeth crowned as well.

After a few short months of some peace and quiet and no visits to the dentist I once again had dental issues.

On Wednesday, March 2, 2022 tooth number 9, which is located on the top of the mouth, mysteriously chipped when I was taking off my night guard. I made an unscheduled visit to the dentist and was politely told that I should have teeth numbers 7-10 all bonded since these teeth would continually cause issues in the future. I told the dentist that I would take that under advisement as long as I would have no pain. He declined to tell me whether I would and said I would be back. During this visit he bonded tooth number 9. Damn it, he was correct.

Two months later the tooth chipped again and on Monday, May 9, 2022 I had to have number 9 bonded again. It may seem funny but I began to think of the days when my parents would tell me about the tooth fairy who would visit young children in their sleep and drop off a small amount of cash to replace the lost tooth.

I don't understand why I have never seen the tooth fairy in the last two years. The only person who seems to visit is the tooth robber who always makes my wallet lighter or my credit card balance higher and higher, and I guess you get the point.

On Tuesday, June 7, 2022 I had my semiannual teeth cleaning. At this appointment the dental hygienist took a full set of x-rays and told me that my teeth and the crowns were all looking fine and I should continue to floss daily. She also gingerly reminded me that my next dental appointment would be the next day to begin crown preparation for teeth numbers 2 and 3.

On Wednesday, June 8, 2022 the dentist and I had another one of our frank conversations and he reminded me that all of the dental work (I call it pain and suffering) would be worth it in the end when my fourteen crowned teeth looked great, functioned great, and gave me a much improved smile.

I already knew the process of crown preparation so rather than bore the readers with all the details I will simply say that I sat back, took a deep breath, and to be tooth full, I grinned and bore the pain. And so began the crown preparation for teeth numbers 2 and 3.

I also made an additional dental appointment for Wednesday, June 29, 2022 to bond tooth number 8 as well as having the permanent crowns for teeth numbers 2 and 3 placed in my mouth. I arrived at the dental office at 8:00 a.m. sharp. No office staff or dental technicians were available to assist the dentist that day so I rescheduled the appointment and all that work to Wednesday, July 6, 2022. On this visit I also decided to play a small practical joke on the dentist before my appointment so feel free to read anecdote #3 (crazy guy in the bathroom) later on in the book.

On that July visit I had one extra thing done, I had pictures taken of teeth 7-10 so the dental office could submit a request from my dental insurance to start my crown work. These would be the last four teeth of a total of fourteen that I would have crowned since my tooth ordeal began.

The dental office received my insurance approval on Thursday, September 1, 2022, more than two years since this dental nightmare began (June 29, 2020). I made an appointment for Thursday, September 15, 2022 to begin the preparation for crowning teeth 7-10 and also to look at teeth 2 and 4 which had been bothering me for the last few weeks. I was informed by the dental manager that it would take approximately three hours to take care of all six teeth. I told her that I would be there with a positive attitude and I was looking forward to the conclusion of this dental journey.

All weekend before that (almost) final appointment with my general dentist I had a lot of trouble sleeping. I tossed and turned knowing what pain was in store for my mouth. I tried to fall asleep and think nothing but good thoughts, but my mind constantly went back to dreaming of Attila the Hun as well as Vlad the Impaler. Attila the Hun was the leader of the Hunnic Empire from 434 to 453 A.D. Also called Flagellum Dei, or the "scourge of God," he was known to Romans for his brutality and a penchant for sacking and pillaging Roman cities.

The other man in my dream was known as Vlad Dracula, son of the Dragon, and, most famously, Vlad the Impaler (Vlad Tepes in Romanian). He was a brutal, sadistic leader famous for torturing his foes. By some estimates he is responsible for the deaths of more than eighty thousand people in his lifetime—a large percentage of them by impalement.

Don't get me wrong. While I am not of course comparing my very professional and highly educated general dentist to an infamous torturer (really, I'm not!) I do see some similarities in the kind of tools or instruments they used on their intended victims. The only difference I can determine is that Vlad and Attila (and no I am in no way related to either of them) wanted to main, torture, and kill, while my dentist only inflicted pain and suffering if my mouth wasn't completely numbed up with novocaine.

On Thursday, September 15, 2022, I walked up the stairs to

my dental office and slowly placed myself in the hallway. I knew quite well that my two-plus years of appointments was soon to be over. I opened the door and pronounced to all in the office, "It is I, your most loyal patient, ready for some torture." They all looked up at me and smiled. I said good morning, let the dance begin.

Teeth 7, 8, 9, and 10 were prepared for crowns; the surface of tooth number 2 was smoothed out and a filling in tooth number 4 was replaced. I was in the dental office for two-plus hours in some discomfort but to be quite honest the dentist and his dental assistant were both and have always been extremely professional, courteous, and are always looking out for the best interests of the patient. I left the office with a small headache, swollen gums, and slight discomfort. I did, however, know that my dental journey was in the final stages and I eagerly awaited the end. My gums around teeth 7-10 were swollen and began to hurt. The filling replaced in tooth number 4 also felt somewhat uncomfortable. I called the dentist and he told me via the telephone that the pain in my tooth was common and would take some time to subside.

In the next few weeks or so every time I heard either my house or cell phone ring I eagerly answered, hoping that the call would be from my dental office informing me that my final four crowns for teeth numbers 7-10 arrived. Actually when I received the phone call on Monday, October 3, 2022 around 9:15 a.m. the office manager said that the permanent crowns wouldn't be in until Thursday, October 6, 2022. The next appointment slot available was Wednesday, October 12, 2022. This date wasn't good since we would be having a family friend staying with us visiting from California. I was then told I could come into the office for my final dental appointment regarding my crowns on Monday, October 17, 2022 at 8:45 a.m. The office manager simply stated that "the case was in." I wondered why she said these words—did she mean a case of diet coke, or a case of tomatoes?—but of course I realized that she meant my new crowns. I made the appointment and could hardly settle down. I was very excited that the tooth journey would finally be concluded.

The day my phone rang and I was informed that my final dental appointment (two years in the making) had arrived, I felt great. I was excited and nervous all at the same time. A slew of emotions overcame me as the long and painful journey down the "Dental Road" was about to end. Many people would probably say, "What is the big deal with having fourteen teeth crowned along with numerous other teeth issues?" Many people would say that getting into their college of choice, getting married, or having a baby is something to get excited and emotional about. While I wholeheartedly agree about these accomplishments, imagine how I felt the day that my two-plus-year journey from the abyss and back was about to conclude.

Without telling the dentist or the office staff I went to the local discount store early that afternoon and purchased a bunch of gag gifts to give the dentist after he successfully permanently cemented on the new crowns for teeth numbers 7-10. As you probably surmised by now I do have a funny sense of humor. In the small backpack that I planned on giving the dentist were the following items:

- **Latex gloves**: to keep the dentist's hands clean and germ free
- **Confetti**: to celebrate this most momentous occasion
- **A rather long and sharp knife**: to slice some nice cake to celebrate the end of my journey, or to cut off a patient's ear if they misbehave in the dental chair
- **A shiny new pair of pliers**: to pull and yank out a tooth
- **A pair of scissors**: in case I ask for a haircut while asleep in the chair
- **A pack of toothbrushes**: to keep the dentist's teeth clean and food free

Gag gift items

- **A container of toothpicks**: for the dentist to pick his teeth or to look cool
- **A package of dental floss**: for the obvious reason

As for the final two small gag gifts—don't ask me why—they were an at-home marijuana drug test and, even though my dentist is male, a very quick ovulation predictor.

FINAL PART OF MY TWO-PLUS YEARS' JOURNEY

Later on Monday, October 3, 2022, the day I got the call to set up my glorious final appointment, around 3:00 p.m. my mouth began to hurt somewhat. The gums around teeth 7-10 were becoming more inflamed and the slight discomfort in tooth number 4 also was getting a little worse. I called the dental office back and was lucky enough to schedule an appointment for Wednesday, October 5, 2022 at 8:00 a.m. to look at my mouth and find out why this was happening.

Even though that day is the most solemn religious fast of the Jewish year, it is also the last of the ten days of penitence that began with Rosh Hashanah (the Jewish new year). I told myself that G-d wouldn't be to mad at me since I was going to a dental appointment for my health, and that he would probably forgive me.

On Wednesday, October 5, 2022, at 8:00 a.m., I arrived at the dentist to have him look at my irritated gums and tooth number 4. The dentist showed up few minutes after. He told me the gum issues were normal since the temporary crowns are made of flexible yet durable plastic resin and can irritate the gums. As for number 4, he said that it looked fine and would take time to settle down. He further said that the tooth's outer layers, called enamel and cementum, protect the nerve from exposure. The filling can get close to the nerve endings and cause irritation and uncomfortable sensations. This eventually goes away but may take a few weeks to settle down. I said thank you and goodbye and left the office in a hurry.

The week before Monday, October 15, 2022 my wife and I had a relative visiting us from Los Angeles. We had a great time showing him all around the smallest but greatest state in the nation.

The day he arrived he had a few small sniffles but told me that he was simply suffering from allergies. Just to be safe I had him take an at-home Covid test and did the same. By the time he left to fly back to LA on Thursday, October 13, 2022 I began to not feel well. My nose began to run; I got sniffles and a slight headache. By late afternoon my ears began to hurt. At the wise suggestion and counsel of the wife, I contacted my doctor who suggested I come in to the office early Friday morning October 14, 2022. Of course when I arrived I was given the routine exam which consisted of blood pressure, temp, oxygen levels, and all seemed fine. When the doctor checked my sinuses and ears I was given the news. I had a severe sinus infection and fluid in both ears. As my doctor and I have a great relationship he also told me after looking into my ear that I had fluid buildup and would need to be on azithromycin and another antibiotic to clear up the infection. I asked if it would be okay to go to my dental appointment on Monday, October 15, 2022 and he boldly exclaimed, "Of course."

The reader might ask why I included the above story about my sinus infection. I simply state that if I couldn't have kept my final dental appointment on Monday, October 17, 2022 I would have been very disappointed.

Over the weekend after taking my antibiotics and the careful, and constant attention from the love of my life I began to feel much better.

Of course I thought that the weekend would be enjoyable and I would not have any dental issues to complain about. Believe you me, I was counting on it. But wait, there's more to my never-ending tooth story.

While eating dinner on Saturday evening I went against the advice of my wise counsel (my wife). She advised me not to eat any items that were hard or chewy, and to cut up dinner in small pieces, and not to bite down on my four front temporary crowns (7-10). Did I listen? No, of course not. I put a large pretzel in my mouth and crunched down with my top front teeth. I was imitating one of the old time greats of comedy, Julius Henry, aka Groucho Marx. In a few short seconds I realized, uh-oh. I had chipped teeth 9 and 10. Barbara then diplomatically mentioned to me the two most important rules in a lengthy and successful marriage: Rule One (your wife is always correct), and Rule Two (refer to Rule One). I was slightly embarrassed and annoyed with myself. I was lucky that my final dental appointment would be in two short days. I could wait and grin and bear the slight discomfort. Ain't that the tooth?

MONDAY, OCTOBER 17, 2022
(A DAY TO REMEMBER—AT LEAST FOR ME)

Monday, October 17, 2022 was a day to remember, at least for me, the author.

On this day, one that went down in history for my mouth and all its thirty-two inhabitants, teeth 7, 8, 9, and 10 were Permanently Crowned.

I entered the dental office at 8:45 a.m. sharp. I felt pretty good that day as I knew that without any additional issues my final four crowns would be permanently cemented on and this chapter in my long book of life would soon be ending.

I had waited over two years to have all of my dental issues resolved. To be more precise I waited 840 days, 27 months, and 2 weeks; or 20,160 hours; or 1,209,600 minutes. I guess you get the point. It's been a damn long time

I sat in the dental chair and the dental assistant, a very lovely lady, had a very calming nature and made me feel slightly relaxed. She hums gently while she works and she always made me feel very comfortable when I was in the chair. She proceeded to remove the temporary crowns with tools that looked like they came out of a horror movie. After a few minutes of waiting the dentist came in and said "The time is now to make your smile beautiful once again." He had the assistant take numerous x-rays of my top four teeth to make sure that the new crowns fit properly. Before I knew it the permanent crowns were cemented in place and to be quite honest I felt great. It seemed that a heavy weight had finally been lifted off my shoulders as two years plus were over. The dentist scheduled me for one final appointment on Monday, October 31,

2022 at 8:00 a.m. to check the crowns one more time and make sure that the swelling in my gums had diminished. Of all days, the final appointment would be on Halloween.

After my appointment I spoke to the dental manager and then went to my car to get my gift for the dentist as well as for the office staff to thank them for all of their patience and friendship the last two years.

The dentist and his assistant hugged me and said that I was a great patient and never complained too much during the last two-plus years. I told them I appreciated all that they did for me.

Finally on Monday, October 31, 2022, at 8:00 a.m., I arrived at the dentist's office for one final checkup to check the last four dental crowns on teeth 7-10 along with the other ten permanent crowns. The dentist simply stated all was well. The dental saga was finally over.

I was given the usual speech about not eating anything sticky or chewy and to avoid popcorn at all costs. I also was told to brush my teeth after every meal and don't forget to always floss. After a few brief words and handshakes, I simply said thank you and left the office for the final time as related to my dental crowns.

IS THE JOURNEY FINALLY OVER??

SO FINALLY after (forty-five dental appointments) I can honestly say that I could have bitten off more than I could chew, but in the end I have a healthy attitude, a healthy smile, and the tooth has finally been told.

I wish you all peace and happiness in all that you undertake.

COMMENTS ABOUT MY
TEETH ISSUES FROM ANYONE
AND EVERYONE WHO CAME ALONG
WITH ME DURING MY JOURNEY

It may seem quite irrational that during my two-plus years of dental appointments and the enormous amount of cost, personal pain and suffering, and time spent on my pearly whites, the three most common questions asked of me are as follows:

1. Did you sue the dentist?
2. Did you sue the dentist?

And last but not least,

3. Did you sue the dentist?

The tooth of the matter is while I was tempted to look into possible litigation against (aka suing) the dentist, the periodontist, the endodontist, the oral surgeon and anyone else I met during these last two years, **NO I DID NOT SUE ANYONE**, and that is G-d's honest tooth. The majority of my dental issues actually began many moons ago when I would grind and chomp down on my teeth and didn't get fitted for a night guard any earlier despite one being suggested by my dentist on numerous occasions. It also didn't help that I would chew on hard candy, crush walnuts and other peanuts with my pearly whites, or it could simply be a combination of all of these items plus genetics.

I found it so odd and occasionally funny that except for family and a few close friends, I can count on my fingertips the times I was asked the following questions:

1. How do you feel?
2. Are you in any pain?
3. How many more dental visits do you have?
4. Do you need a ride to any appointments?
5. Do you get headaches?
6. Are you sure you're feeling okay?
7. Do you need me to cut your food into small bitty pieces so you can gum your dinner? (Only joking!)

I can honestly tell you that the majority of the questions asked of me were related to whether or not I was suing anyone; that is a sad testament to the fast moving society that we live in today.

Now that I have bored you with my story I will include some definitions, the origins of tooth care and the numerous types of dentists that may help the reader to a better understanding of this profession.

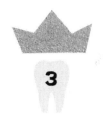

3

ORIGIN OF
TAKING CARE OF TEETH

The author is including a few facts about teeth and early dental care, types of dentists that were referred to throughout the book, and some dental definitions to help the reader better understand dental issues such as crowns and root canals.

WHAT ARE TEETH MADE OF?

Human teeth are made up of four different types of tissue. **Dentin, enamel,** and **cementum** are hard tissues. The **pulp** is the innermost portion of the tooth and consists of connective tissue, nerves, and blood vessels, which nourish the tooth.

ORIGIN OF TEETH BRUSHING

When did humans start brushing their teeth?
The first toothbrush was likely developed **around 3000 BCE.** This was a frayed twig developed by the Babylonians and the Egyptians. Other sources have found that around 1600 BCE, the Chinese created sticks from aromatic trees' twigs to help freshen their breath.

Did cavemen brush their teeth?

Cavemen chewed on sticks to clean their teeth and even used grass stalks to pick in between their teeth. Without the availability of high-quality toothbrushes and toothpaste, however, a caveman's teeth were more susceptible to cavities and decay, even with a healthy, carbohydrate-free diet.

How did people deal with cavities in the old days?

The simple answer is they didn't. Most times the tooth was pulled out and the issue was over.

The first dentists were barbers and blacksmiths

Both blacksmiths and barbers had the tools necessary to pull teeth—the only way people back then dealt with a toothache.

How did they fix teeth in ancient times?

Some of the early techniques in these cultures included chewing on bark or sticks with frayed ends, feathers, fish bones, and porcupine quills. They used materials like silver, jade, and gold to repair or decorate their teeth.

DENTISTRY

What is a dentist?

According to the Merriam-Webster dictionary, a dentist is a professional who is skilled in and licensed to practice the prevention, diagnosis, and treatment of diseases, injuries, and malformations of the teeth, jaws, and mouth and who makes and inserts false teeth.

Why are people afraid of the dentist?

Fear of pain. (Look up the phrase dental pain and you may find a picture of the author) Fear of pain is a very common reason for avoiding the dentist. This fear usually stems from an early dental experience that was unpleasant or painful, or from dental "pain and horror" stories told by others.

Humiliation. Some people are embarrassed if someone looks at their teeth.

Why going to the dentist is extremely important

It prevents future dental problems, saves your teeth, and helps you achieve a nice smile and increase your self-esteem, like my friend below who is affectionately called "Horse of Course."

Types of dentists in modern times

General Dentist: Your primary dental care provider, usually the first person you will call when your teeth hurt.

Endodontist: Specializes in tooth pain, disease, and infection.

Periodontist: Treats gum inflammation.

Oral Surgeon: Treats problems of the mouth, jaw, face, and neck.

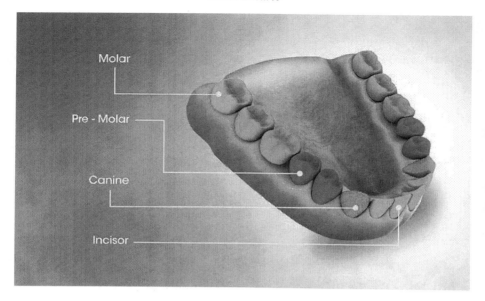

Cost to go to dental school

You may not care or have any interest in what it costs to become a dental professional, but it may help you understand why one of the main reasons so many people don't go to a dentist is Cost. According to the American Dental Association the average cost to attend four years of dental school is anywhere from $151,508 for an in-state public school to $268,348 to attend a private dental school. It of course will be substantially greater if the dentist goes on to further his education in order to specialize.

Types of Teeth and Their Functions

The following is probably useless information for most of us but I thought I could briefly tell you the types of teeth in your mouth and the purpose for each of them.

Incisors: Your incisors are the eight teeth in the front center of your mouth (four on both bottom and top). These teeth are chisel shaped and have sharp edges. Their main function is to bite pieces of food. These teeth greet your family and friends and are in most

(NO. Not this type of canine) "WOOF"

of your photographs when you smile. These are the teeth that you use to chomp down on sweet corn and well-done cheeseburgers at the family picnic.

Canines: Your canines are the next teeth that develop and are on either side of your incisors. These teeth are slightly more pointed than incisors, and their functions are similar. The term "canine" conjures up a rabid dog, which is far from reality.

Premolars: These teeth are located behind your canines and have two points (cusps) and one or two roots. They are used for tearing and grinding food.

Molars: These teeth are located in the back of your mouth and have four or five cusps and two or three roots and are used for chewing and grinding food. Your molars are your largest teeth.

Wisdom teeth: These teeth usually emerge between the ages of seventeen and twenty-one or a more mature age. If you remember having pain in your back teeth in your teens, it was most likely your wisdom teeth, also known as your third molars. They are the last teeth to arrive, usually when you are young. If they erupt straight out, then they usually don't have to be removed. However, if they don't erupt in the correct way, they can cause pain and infection and will need to be removed.

4

DEFINITIONS

Crown: This is a cap that goes over your existing tooth to protect it from further damage.

Dental Crown Procedure: The dentist examines the tooth, files it down, and takes an impression so the crown will fit on the remaining tooth structure.

Tooth Bonding: This doesn't refer to dentists emotionally bonding over their shared interest in teeth. It's a procedure used to repair teeth cracks or chips.

Tooth Decay: This doesn't refer to the letters in the alphabet ("D" and "K").

Causes include bacteria, snacking, sipping sugary drinks, and poor teeth cleaning.

There may be no symptoms. Untreated cavities can cause toothache, infection, and tooth loss. Treatments include fluoride, fillings, and crowns. Severe cases may need a root canal or removal.

I assume you remember when your parents would say quit eating all of that candy, such as fireballs, jawbreakers, or gumballs.

You should have listened to their sage advice. You probably didn't like it—I didn't—and you were always arguing with them and did not pay close attention.

Tooth Extraction: Not much to say about this, but to put it simply, a real pain. It is when the man in the white coat with a large needle and pair of pliers yanks out your bad tooth.

Dental Crown Cost: Hope you have dental insurance or an unlimited credit card.

The price of a dental crown averages from $1,100 to $1,725 but can vary widely depending on the patient's dental insurance and if the crown is paid for without insurance coverage. The biggest factor in a dental crown's cost is the substance it's made of: porcelain, ceramic, metal, or a combination.

Root Canal Procedure: Root canal treatment is when the tooth is drilled and any infected matter is removed.

Root Canal Cost: On average, the cost of a root canal treatment on a front tooth is around $1,000; for bicuspids, it's about $1,100. Molars, in the back, are harder to reach and clean. Root canal treatments in those teeth typically cost the most. Prices are usually **$1,300 to $1,600.**

MAYA'S QUOTES
AND COMMENTS

My eleven-year-old granddaughter is witty, intelligent, pretty, smart, and has a way with words; sometimes she's a little fresh, but always funny. I usually write down some of her witticisms, quotes, and comments and would love to share some with you now. Maya calls me Papa and she calls her grandmother Bubba.

"Rude," with heavy emphasis.

"How Dare You?"

"Papa you're too good at changing the subject."

"Stop clicking your teeth."

"No No."

"It's not happening."

"Stop tapping."

"Stop banging your walking stick on the street when we walk Harry the Dog. You're making too much noise."

Knowing I have a serious allergy to tomatoes she says to me on occasion, "Why don't you eat some tomatoes, he he he!!!"

"Can I have this please?" When we go shopping at any store, Maya always shines a bright smile and asks this.

"Stop calling Sally a boy when you know she's a girl."

"Stop calling Harry (our male dog) a girl when you know he's a boy."

"Thanks old man." Maya likes to tell me that I am 611 years old plus.

When I ask Maya, "How do you know that I love you?" she just responds, "I just know."

"Baba, Papa has the whipped cream can again."

"You can't make me do that."

"Stop showing me your teeth."

"Papa I don't want to see your teeth."

"Papa your head looks like a hard-boiled egg."

"Bubba, Papa has the ice cream again."

When Baba was going down to the basement Papa asked Baba if she needed help, to which Maya said, "Papa, what do you think she needs, protection?"

When Papa and Maya were taking a walk on the way home, I asked Maya to open the door of the house with my key and she replied "Papa you're so predictable."

"Papa, Baba can do whatever she wants."

"Chill out Papa."

When I ask Maya who is the boss she says Bubba then Maya and Harry and Sally. When I ask Maya why not Papa she replies, "Very funny Papa, you know you're not the boss and never will be."

"Papa, you ask too many questions."

"Papa, you have too many rules."

In Walmart I told Maya to give me her hand since it's a busy parking, to which she replied, "Papa, straighten up, relax, and take a deep breath and calm down."

"Papa, am I still in your will?"

"Yes, you are Maya."

"Don't spend too much of your money."

One day as Papa and Baba were in the Walmart parking lot,

Maya asked "Can I get a toy?" Whereas Papa tells Maya money doesn't grow on trees, Maya responds "Yes it does, because paper is made from trees and money comes from paper." At that point Papa says, "Okay Maya, you can spend ten dollars in the store."

When Baba asked Maya if she could have a sleepover at Maya's house, Maya responded, "You have to bring your own bed and sleeping bag."

My most favorite comment of all from my eleven-year-old granddaughter: "I'm the only granddaughter that you have and you should cherish me." We do.

And as I leave the reader with some of my granddaughter's funny comments I end with one of her favorites: "I'm done with this conversation."

6

POETRY

A few poems submitted by friends, relatives, and one by the author, all somewhat related to my lengthy tooth issues.

RUSSIAN POETRY

My father-in-law loves candy.
Because of it, he goes to the dentist a lot.

Maria—09.09.2022

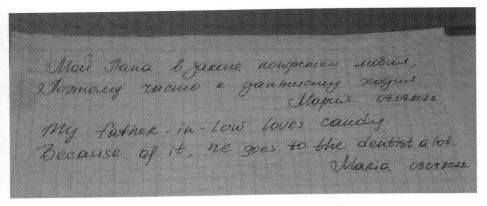

Submitted by Maria Dwares, my daughter-in-law

Kevin Dwares

BAD NEWS BOY

I went to the dentist
'cuz I couldn't sleep
I was hoping to solve
apnea during my sleep.

So I went for a cure.
The Dentist said he
could do it for sure.
But the "Oasis" he gave me
Was not a saving grace
More like a mirage
it was not a real place.
I tried this device
which didn't feel nice.
It wore down my teeth
I had root canals twice.

After three thousand dollars
and multiple visits
I said I was angry
actually livid.
I wanted my money back
but he wasn't obliging
And after I insisted
I saw he was somewhat conniving

Because he handed me two tubes
connected with plastic
Said my nose could breathe better
it was fantastic
ten cents to make
and did I not mention
I was in for six thousand more
already
for braces from the tension
that the Oasis caused
by moving my bite
I was stuck with invisalign
which invaded my life.

Now I am in for 10K
and with a retainer forever.
All because of the dentist
who wasn't too clever.

And way too greedy
for the obviously needy
So watch out for your pocketbook
when they are fixing your mouth
You would think you'd look north
But it all could go south!

Submitted by Chai May. Contact her at Praying Naked: A Women's Journey Without Shame (Facebook)

MY ACHY BREAKY TEETH

I'm sitting in the dental chair on this very nice day
The only thing I could do is to begin to pray
I am worried again for more and pain and suffering
When I suddenly begin to chat and it appears I am stuttering

The dentist comes in and says how are you today
He tells me I look like a praying mantis, and I exclaim "Oy Vey"
He tells me that all today will be well
I ask "If not do I need to pay the bill?

The dentist himself has barely started
When suddenly he gets up and departed
I wonder where he possibly could be
And he returns in a minute with a pet monkey

I asked him what he is doing
And he exclaims "This is my therapy pet"
"Will he bite?" I ask and the dentist replies?
"Not today, he has finished his lunch and he is all set"

I wonder to myself: am I in the right place?
I then say, "Is this a zoo or a dental practice?"
I guess it's time to conclude this poem
And sit back and begin the novocaine storm

I now realize that I am not a poet
But a patient with a story and I intend to show it
May peace and prosperity bless us all
And end this poem once and for all

Written by the Author Kevin D. Dwares after having a lot of dental work and many novocaine shots.

Haiku: A haiku is an unrhymed Japanese poetic form that consists of seventeen syllables arranged in three lines containing five, seven, and five syllables, respectively. A haiku expresses much and suggests more in the fewest possible words. The form gained distinction in the seventeenth century when Basho, a Japanese poet considered the greatest practitioner of the form, elevated it to a highly refined art. It remains Japan's most popular poetic form. The Imagist poets (1912–30) and others have imitated the form in English and other languages.

HAIKU

The Dental Practice
Oh my poor, sore, sorry mouth
Work on someone else

Brushing, flossing teeth
Good care, we care, crowns we need
Needles, drilling done

Bright smiles, shiny teeth
Happy faces, such a grin
Not sorry, we are done

Submitted by Barbara Dwares

GENESIS

In the beginning of time while G-d himself was thinking about creating the world as we know it, he must have asked himself how mankind would eat to survive and also how they'd take care of all of their body parts and their functions.

G-d created humans with about three hundred bones at birth which include those of the skull, spine (vertebrae), ribs, arms, and legs. These bones eventually will fuse to form the two hundred bones that adults have.

G-d also created humans with a full set of twenty primary teeth (ten in the upper jaw and ten in the lower jaw) hidden under the gums. Primary teeth are also known as baby teeth, milk teeth, or deciduous teeth. By the time a human reaches adulthood they have a full set of thirty-two teeth which include eight incisors, four canines, eight premolars, and twelve molars including four wisdom teeth. These teeth would need to have numerous functions so that man could live a reasonable length of time.

And no disrespect to G-d, I leave you with the below comments.

Sometimes I think G-d should have created humans with indestructible teeth which would last a lifetime, made out of stone, metal, or extremely strong wood. Or at least at birth give us a Free medical and dental insurance policy (worldwide with no deductibles), which would pay for all medical and dental bills from birth to you know what (The End of Life).

8

ROOT OF DENTAL PROBLEMS

REASONS WHY HUMANS
HAVE POOR DENTAL HEALTH

Some people tend to be more prone to tooth problems. You may wonder why, in civilized and democratic societies with billions upon billions of dollars floating around in the medical system, so many people young and old suffer from dental issues. Another thing to wonder: What makes the difference between people who seem to have great teeth and never seem to get a cavity, and others who suffer constantly with dental pain and issues? One of the most common factors is diet.

THE MODERN DIET MAY BE
PARTIALLY TO BLAME

Historically, when humans lived as hunter-gatherers, our ancestors survived on a natural diet. Back then, there were no processed foods, no fast-food restaurants, and our ancestors had wonderful teeth, based on findings. Today a great many people consume tremendous amounts of sugar and junk related food.

This may explain why our modern diet is at least part of the cause of our dental woes.

THE ROLE OF GENETICS

Genetics also contributes a lot to whether one will have a lot of tooth problems. Everyone has a slightly unique body, including the mouth. All you can do is take care of your teeth as best you can and visit the dentist on a regular basis. If you develop teeth problems for one reason or another, at least your dentist will be able to treat the problems in their early stages, before you need fillings for cavities, or root canals or crowns on your teeth.

POLLUTION AND THE ENVIRONMENT

In my own mind, I believe that pollution and the environment may be a cause of dental issues, as well as other medical problems facing us all.

CONCLUSION

I hope that you have enjoyed reading the saga of my teeth entitled *A Royal Crowning Achievement*. Its purpose was simply to tell the reader my story of a two-year journey of sitting in the dental chair. I know that many people may think some of the book was funny and some readers may think that it wasn't funny at all. It was only written to tell my story. I didn't mean to hurt the feelings of anyone who is going or have gone through dental problems. In the end I have learned a rather painful lesson that those of us who wear night guards to protect their teeth from excessive grinding (aka bruxism) should always remember to put it in its container every night. Luckily for me my new night guard is in solitary confinement when I am done wearing it.

While my two-plus-year journey may have had some early dental mishaps, I have chosen to take the high road and not blame anyone for my teeth issues. While having fourteen crowns inserted in my mouth is extreme, I am fortunate enough in that I have dental insurance, my teeth could be corrected, and I can still maintain a nice smile and my dental health. While some people would want to seek out legal recourse I decided that writing this book was very cathartic to me and good for my mental health by allowing me to freely share some of the intense emotions of the last two-plus years.

MY PERSONAL WORDS OF ADVICE

Whether you're afraid of going to the dentist or not (and most people are), go for regular checkups. Brush your teeth after every meal. Take care of your teeth, beginning at an early age, so hopefully you will have fewer problems later on in life. You are your most important advocate for your health. Don't forget your teeth; they serve many purposes in life.

APPENDICES

APPENDIX A

CHARTS

The three charts below were developed by Kevin Dean Dwares to be used as a referral guide only:

Tooth Number	Type Of Tooth	Removed
1	WISDOM	YES
2	CROWN	NO
3	CROWN	NO
4	REGULAR	NO
5	REGULAR	NO
6	REGULAR	NO
7	CROWN	NO
8	CROWN	NO
9	CROWN	NO
10	CROWN	NO
11	REGULAR	NO
12	REGULAR	NO
13	REGULAR	NO
14	REGULAR	NO
15	REGULAR	NO
16	WISDOM	YES
17	WISDOM	YES
18	CROWN	NO
19	CROWN	NO

20	REGULAR	NO
21	REGULAR	NO
22	REGULAR	NO
23	CROWN	NO
24	CROWN	NO
25	CROWN	NO
26	CROWN	NO
27	REGULAR	NO
28	REGULAR	NO
29	REGULAR	NO
30	CROWN	NO
31	CROWN	NO
32	WISDOM	YES

DATE	DENTIST	TOOTH #	DESCRIPTION
Mon. June 29, 2020	N/A	ALL	Harry the dog ate night guard
Tues. June 30, 2020	General Dentist	ALL	Impression of teeth for night guard
Tues. June 30, 2020	General Dentist	27	Bonding of tooth
Tues. June 30, 2020	General Dentist	18	X-ray of tooth #18
Mon. July 06, 2020	General Dentist	30, 31	Crown preparation
Mon. July 20, 2020	General Dentist	30, 31	Crowns inserted
Tues. Aug. 04, 2020	General Dentist	18	X-ray of tooth #18
Tues. Aug. 04, 2020	General Dentist	ALL	Teeth cleaning by dental hygienist
Fri. Aug. 14, 2020	General Dentist	18	Initial crown preparation
Mon. Sept. 14, 2020	General Dentist	18	Crown inserted on tooth #18
Fri. Sept. 18, 2020	General Dentist	18	Called dentist who prescribed ibuprofen
Sat. Sept. 19, 2020	General Dentist	18	Called dentist who prescribed azithromycin
Mon. Sept. 21, 2020	General Dentist	18	Appointment to look at tooth #18 (again)
Thurs. Sept. 22, 2020	Endodontist	18	Root canal
Fri. Oct. 02, 2020	Periodontist	18	X-ray of tooth #18
Fri. Oct. 02, 2020	Oral Surgeon	18	Evaluate tooth #18
Mon. Oct. 05, 2020	General Dentist	19	Crown preparation
Thurs. Oct. 08, 2020	Oral Surgeon	18	Review of #18 to determine removal

Date	Provider	Tooth	Description
Tues. Oct. 20, 2020	Oral Surgeon	18	Decision time for #18
Thurs. Oct. 22, 2020	General Dentist	19	Crown inserted
Mon. Nov. 02, 2020	Dental Hygienist	ALL	Teeth cleaning by dental hygienist
Mon. Nov. 09, 2020	Periodontist	18	Removal of small piece of tooth fragment
Mon. Nov. 23, 2020	General Dentist	ALL	New night guard
Tues. Dec. 01 ,2020	General Dentist	30	Crown re-cemented back on
Weds. Dec. 09, 2020	General Dentist	8, 9	Teeth bonded
Fri. Dec. 18, 2020	General Dentist	19	Crown fell off
Mon. Dec. 21, 2020	General Dentist	19	Crown temporarily re-cemented back on
Weds. Dec. 30. 2020	General Dentist	18,19	Conference with dental practice
Sun. Jan. 03, 2021	General Dentist	19	Crown fell off while drinking water
Mon. Jan. 04, 2021	General Dentist	18,19	Re-cement #19 and review of #18
Weds. Jan. 06, 2021	General Dentist	18,19	#18, #19 crowns removed, temporary crowns
Tues. Jan 19, 2021	General Dentist	18,19	#18, #19 crowns permanently cemented.
Mon. May 24, 2021	General Dentist	21	Tooth bonding
Thurs. Aug. 05, 2021	General Dentist	27,28	Tooth filling
Weds. Sept. 01, 2021	General Dentist	24	Tooth filling
Thurs. Nov. 04, 2021	General Dentist	25	Tooth filling
Thurs. Dec. 02, 2021	General Dentist	ALL	X-rays and oral exam of all teeth

Date	Provider	Teeth	Procedure
Mon Dec. 13, 2021	General Dentist	23-26	Crown preparation four bottom teeth
Mon. Dec. 20, 2021	General Dentist	25, 26	Crowns permanently inserted
Thurs. Jan. 20, 2022	General Dentist	23,24	Crowns permanently inserted
Thurs. Jan. 20, 2022	General Dentist	2, 3	Fillings replaced
Wed. Mar. 02, 2022	General Dentist	9	Tooth bond
Mon. May 09, 2022	General Dentist	9	Bonding of tooth
Tues. June 07, 2022	General Dentist	ALL	Teeth cleaning by dental hygienist
Wed. June 08 , 2022	General Dentist	2, 3	Crowns preparation
Wed. June 29, 2022	General Dentist	2, 3 (8)	Cancelled due to lack of staff
Wed. July 06, 2022	General Dentist	2, 3	Permanent crowns inserted.
Wed. July 06, 2022	General Dentist	8	Tooth bonded
Wed. July 06, 2022	General Dentist	7-10	Pictures and x-rays taken for insurance
Thurs. Sept. 15, 2022	General Dentist	7-10	Crown preparation
Thurs. Sept. 15, 2022	General Dentist	2, 4	File down chip on #2 and replace filling of #4
Weds. Oct. 05, 2022	General Dentist	4, Gums	Pain in #4 and gum irritation (teeth #7-#10)
Mon. Oct. 17, 2022	General Dentist	7-10	Permanent crowns installed and cemented.
Mon. Oct. 31, 2022	General Dentist	7-10	Final appointment: Mission Complete

Tooth Number	Description
1	Wisdom Tooth (3rd Molar)
2	Molar (2nd Molar)
3	Molar (1st Molar)
4	Bicuspid (2nd)
5	Bicuspid (1st)
6	Canine (Eye tooth/Cuspid)
7	Incisor (Lateral)
8	Incisor (Central)
9	Incisor (Central)
10	Incisor (Lateral)
11	Canine (Eye tooth/Cuspid)
12	Bicuspid (1st)
13	Bicuspid (2nd)
14	Molar (1st Molar)
15	Molar (2nd Molar)
16	Wisdom Tooth (3rd Molar)
17	Wisdom Tooth (3rd Molar)
18	Molar (2nd molar)
19	Molar (1st molar)
20	Bicuspid (2nd)
21	Bicuspid (1st)
22	Canine (Eye tooth/Cuspid)
23	Incisor (Lateral)
24	Incisor (Central)
25	Incisor (Central)
26	Incisor (Lateral)
27	Canine (Eye tooth/Cuspid)
28	Bicuspid (1st)
29	Bicuspid (2nd)
30	Molar (1st Molar)
31	Molar (2nd Molar)
32	Wisdom Tooth (3rd Molar)

APPENDIX B

PICTURES

The below pictures and hand-drawn sketches by friends and relatives are meant to add some levity to my book.

The author hard at work diligently developing Excel spreadsheets

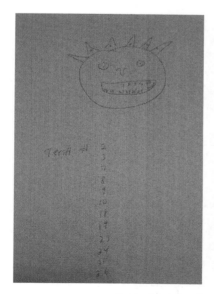

Original drawings by the author. As you can tell
he has ZERO artistic abilities.

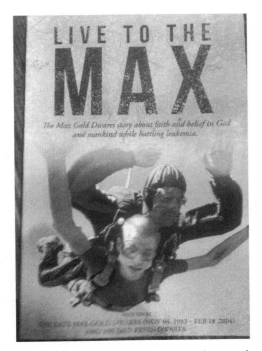

Picture of author's first book entitled Live to the Max about his son's battle with leukemia. Max passed away at the age of twenty on February 18, 2004 from complications.

Picture of Max around age seventeen.

Picture of my granddaughter, Maya.

Picture of night guard case

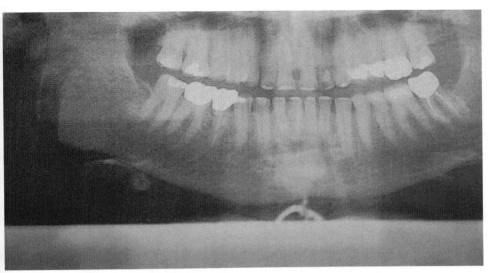

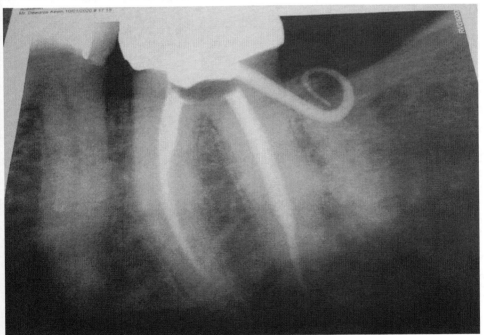

Top: *Actual panoramic photo of the author's teeth. Notice far right tooth number 18. This tooth began the dental journey.*
Bottom: *Actual photo of the root canal of tooth 18.*

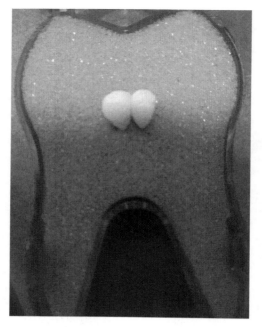

Actual picture of temporary crowns for teeth numbers 23 and 24.

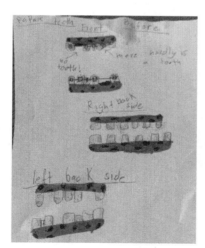
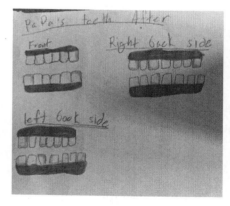

Left: *Granddaughter Maya's drawing of the author's*
(Papa's) teeth prior to a lot of the dental work.
Right: *Granddaughter Maya's drawing of the author's*
(Papa's) teeth after all of the dental work.

Picture of author on his way to a dental appointment.

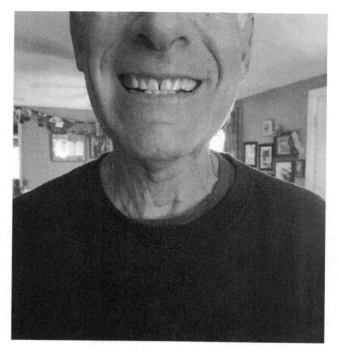

Picture of teeth 7-10 before any dental work (sometime in 2020).

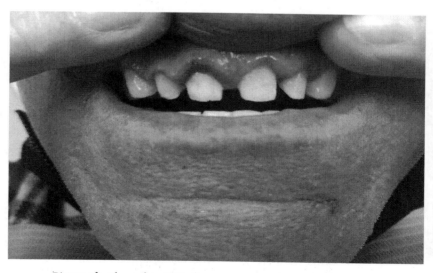

Picture of teeth numbers 7-10 after crown preparation. Not a pretty smile but what needed to be done to allow permanent crowns to be put on teeth. (Thursday, September 15, 2022)

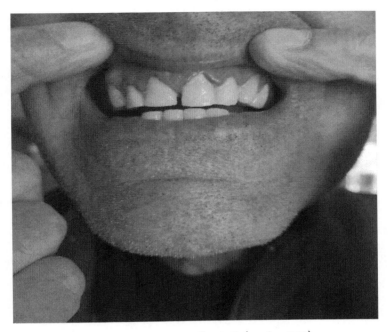

Temporary crowns on top four teeth (numbers 7-10).
(Thursday, September 15, 2022)

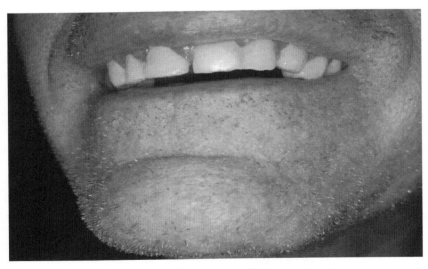

Picture of chipped tooth number 9 after foolishly munching down on a pretzel while imitating comedian legend "Groucho Marx" after dinner on Saturday, October 15, 2022.

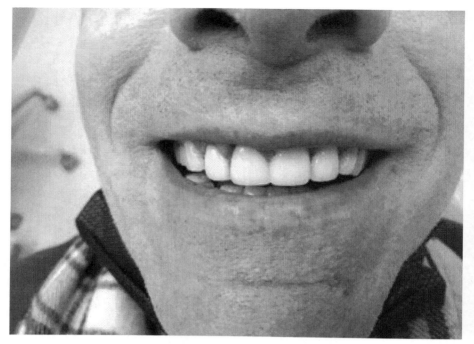

Final permanent crowns on top four teeth (numbers 7-10). It's been a long time from June 29, 2020 to today (October 17, 2022).

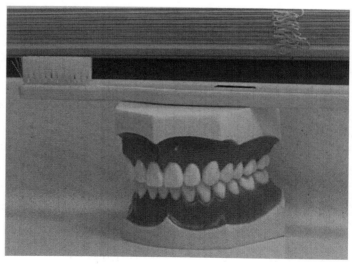

Funny teeth and toothbrush in dental office (October 15, 2022)

APPENDIX C

QUOTES

I've been to the dentist many times, so I know the drill.

Lying through your teeth does not count as flossing.

If you have more cavities than you have teeth, you've led a sweet life.

A good dentist never gets on your nerves.

My dentist always gets to the root of the problem.

Why do hockey players never smile? It's because one tooth doesn't look good.

As my dentist approaches me with his dental pick, he says "I will get to the point sooner or later"
—submitted by Barbara Dwares

*The chair is leaned back. The patient's mouth is full of cotton and the water extractor. The dentist approaches and asks your opinion of current events and you respond "##$$^%&&&^**A&*&"!!!!!!*

Be true to your teeth and they won't be false to you.

Dentistry is not expensive...neglect is.

"If you tell the tooth you don't have to remember anything."
—Mark Twain

Always remember the most famous quote of all:
"The tooth will set you free."

To tell the Tooth.

Tooth or Consequences.

Tooth or Dare.

Awful Tooth (1937 comedy starring Gary Grant and Irene Dunn)

I swear to tell the tooth and nothing but the tooth.

You can't handle the tooth (starring Jack Nicolson in A Few Good Men).

The tooth is out there.

The tooth will set you free, but not until it is finished with you.

It is better to tell the tooth and face the punishment, than to lie and suffer the consequences.

Tooth is always painful unless you accept it.

And finally, one of my favorite quotes about the tooth:
The tooth is rarely pure and never simple.

ANECDOTES

If you'll pardon me I will tell you a few short true stories involving my dental professionals that happened during my two years of experiences with them. To be quite frank with you (and I don't mean Hebrew National, if you get the pun), I am somewhat ashamed of myself for some of the anecdotes that you will read below. Considering I was persevering through two years of pain and suffering and a constant mouth throbbing and headache you will forgive me (I hope).

1) MEETING NEW DENTIST IN THE HALLWAY (WITH HIS MASK ON)

Sometime around mid-September through October 2020, (I can't remember the actual date) I was in the interim general dentist's office with the little blue spit apron around my neck. I was having one of my usual painful dental experiences and felt a tremendous urge to use the bathroom. Halfway through my appointment. I told the dentist and I was told to take the bib off and go down the hallway. I didn't graciously reply about taking off my spit bib and instead ran out the door.

While in the hallway going down towards the men's room a gentleman came up to me wearing a mask and put his hand on my shoulder and proceeded to remove my spit bib. I said to him in rather unpleasant words who the hell are you to touch me. Covid is going around and I don't want anyone putting their hands on my neck or getting anywhere near my face. The man looked somewhat startled, and then began to apologize and proceeded to say to me, "I am the new dentist and I will be taking over the dental practice in the next week or so and the interim dentist will be leaving the dental practice as well." Oh, I thought to myself at that moment, he's the guy who could cause me pain, torture, and suffering in the future, so at that point I simply said to him welcome to the neighborhood and I am glad to make your acquaintance.

I decided that after my appointment that day I would apologize to the new dentist and just explain how I felt with all the dental work that I had been experiencing. He said that he wasn't upset with me and understood how I felt.

I left the office shortly thereafter and went next door to the liquor store and came back with an assortment of goodies and a bottle or two of liquor for the dentist and the staff. Since that day the dentist and I have become friends and we always tell jokes and stories every time I am in his office. He always likes to tell people about the day I met him in the hallway. After all I always try to make a good impression, especially in the dentist's office.

2) PLAYING DEAD IN THE CHAIR

On Wednesday, January 6, 2021 I had dental crowns removed from teeth numbers 18 and 19 in a very painful procedure. I had the two new crowns permanently cemented on Tuesday, January 19, 2021. The below anecdote is my short and amusing story, at least when it's told from my perspective. **PLEASE** I don't recommend that anyone pull the stunt that I did. It was wrong, somewhat hurtful and a little immature. If you ask me do I regret it, and do I feel bad, the short answer is somewhat. But if you ask me if I am glad that I scared the crap out of the dentist and the dental technicians, I would have to be honest and say it was the best five minutes that I had ever experienced and a once in a lifetime opportunity. It was, I would like to say in one short phrase, "Priceless and Outrageous." Was it all a dream or a nightmare? Did the novocaine shots in my system make me have hallucinations? You be the judge!

I have been known to fall asleep within two or three minutes. The most memorable times were when my wife and I went to see the movie *The French Lieutenant's Woman* starring Meryl Streep, and seeing Jerry Seinfeld at PPAC in Providence, Rhode Island. When I get bored or am tired the lights go out in a hurry, if you get my drift.

This time I was in the dental torture chamber (dental office) and was given numerous shots of novocaine to numb my upper lip for the impending removal of the crowns of teeth 18 and 19. I hope that I never again have to have any dental crowns removed.

I feigned being fast asleep and heard the dentists call out my name. I didn't respond at first and they were quite nervous and concerned. I heard them say to give me some smelling salts if I didn't come out of my deep sleep. The dentist also told the office manager to get ready to call 911 if I didn't respond. I opened my eyes and asked what was going on. They seemed worried about me. I should have told them that I was of course faking being asleep but I didn't. Suffice to say, I never played that stunt again.

3) PLAYING "CRAZY GUY" IN THE BATHROOM

This actually happened on the way into my dentist's office on Wednesday, July 6, 2022 at 8:00 a.m. to have my two new crowns for teeth numbers 2 and 3 cemented in.

On that day at home before I left for the dentist, I was feeling a little frustrated as I was having work done on teeth 9 and 10 too. I was getting mad at myself and the whole damn situation with all my dental issues so then and there, I decided to vent a little to Barbara (wife) and to play a little joke on my dentist. Barbara emphatically said to me that I shouldn't do anything of the sort and that I should always follow the high road and do nothing that would be considered immature, ignorant, or childlike. Hmm, I thought, since I love *The Three Stooges* from television reruns I will act out like they did. I went into my toolbox and took out a pair of shiny pliers to bring with me to the dental office that morning. To be quite honest with you I felt great and decided that I should never have any regrets in life, never show fear, and at that moment determined that the deed had to be done. It would probably make me feel a little better even though the actual act would begin and end within thirty seconds or so.

I knew that my dentist usually arrived at the office a few minutes after 8:00 a.m. and always went into the bathroom down the hall to make sure his Covid-19 mask was on correctly.

I decided to go into the bathroom stall and put on dark sunglasses, a Covid-19 mask, and a baseball cap. When I heard the dentist open the door and hum to himself I knew I had twenty-five seconds or so to react. I took the shiny pliers out of my jacket pocket, held them in my right hand, opened the door, and loudly pronounced "I am Michael Myers from the Halloween movies and I am here to finish business."

The dentist looked at me and actually thought for a moment that I was a crazed lunatic. He asked me to calm down as he hurriedly exited the bathroom and ran down the hall. I wasn't sure at first if he knew that it was me, his patient.

When I finally went down the hall, laughing my ass off, I entered the office as I heard him explain to his medical staff that a nutcase was trying to scare the crap out of him. When he realized it was me he asked me, "You weren't really trying to hurt me were you?" I responded, "Not unless you hurt me while I am in your chair having another dental procedure." Yuk, Yuk, Yuk.

Well what can I say about this short anecdote? Was I sorry that I scared the dentist with my pliers? Was I sorry for being immature and ignorant? Should I apologize for my behavior? NO. NO. NO. I actually kept the pliers on my lap the entire time in the dental chair. Needless to say I was laughing inside the entire time, and to tell you the tooth, I loved every minute of it. Would I recommend all patients go to their appointments with a pair of pliers or any other sharp and pointed instrument? No of course not, but I must admit it was the most fun and exhilaration I had had for a long time. Do I have any regrets? NAH!

4) MEETING MY SON'S ORTHODONTIST FROM MANY YEARS AGO.

This actually happened on Saturday, September 17, 2022 in a local supermarket while my wife and I were shopping. While walking towards the checkout register a man began to pass me with his shopping cart filled with groceries. He was wearing a face mask but he looked somewhat familiar. At first I couldn't remember his name or where I knew him from. For some odd reason I asked him what his first name was. He replied and I opened my mouth as wide as possible and showed him my pearly whites, including, of course, my newly installed temporary crowns on teeth numbers 7-10. These are the four most prominent teeth at the top of your mouth. I suddenly realized that he was my son Jake's orthodontist from many years ago when he had to get braces on his teeth (a very good investment indeed). The exact reply from the orthodontist was this: "Wow, whoever put on those temporary crowns is very professional and did a great job. I would highly recommend him and his dental work to anyone." After that comment we exchanged a few simple pleasantries and went about our business and left the store.

FINAL THOUGHTS

I hope that you have enjoyed my saga in *A Royal Crowning Achievement*. I know that some of you may have found my story funny, entertaining, and somewhat laughable. Well that was the point of the story.

Some of you may have not liked my saga at all. That is of course your prerogative.

For anyone going through serious medical or dental issues I would like to apologize if you felt that I was being insensitive to your pain and suffering. That wasn't my point at all. If you were offended by any or the entirety of my story, then I honestly can say that I am sorry.

For those of you, if any, who found that my personal experience perhaps helped you to articulate your own feelings, then I am grateful and humbled.

I leave you with these brief quotes that I have come across from time to time, along with a few of my own thoughts.

Life is for the living. Life isn't the destination at the end, but the journey everyone always takes. It's best to live with a little humor in life but be a good soul while down here on solid ground.

I have learned a few important things about myself and I hope you don't mind if I share some of them now:

The life that you live is more important than the lifestyle you choose to live.

Don't get so busy working to make a living that you forget to make a life.

People, me and many others, tend to ask G-d for things, like health, wealth, and happiness. I think it would be better to look inwards to yourself and realize that G-d has already bestowed upon us all of these qualities and many more.

Don't live your life with regrets. The path untraveled may have given you more happiness than one could ever have imagined.

Don't keep all your omissions and fears inside of you. They tend to bog you down and may keep you from the incredible journey your life will become.

Live the only life that you have been given. Remember that life is for the living.

I wish you nothing but good health and happiness. Everyone simply wants to live as pain free a life as possible and leave behind a great legacy for generations to come. I leave you with these final words:

I think that all that people really want is to be loved and be able to love. Reach out to someone, say hello, lend a helping hand, call a family member not just in times of need but at any time. I think sometimes we think that the world we live in is spinning so fast and we all want to see the advancements in medicine and technology and many great accomplishments that we sometimes forget. But we also must not forget to treat our fellow human beings with dignity, compassion, understanding, and civility, no matter who they are, what gender or sexual orientation they are.

The last two-plus years of my life from June 29, 2020 until October 31, 2022 seemed like an eternity. I made countless phone calls, had many appointments, dealt with many insurance and financial issues, had many sore gums, hurting teeth, and headaches.

But, in the end all of the pain and suffering was well worth it. I had my teeth corrected which led to a healthier mouth and a new and improved smile on my face.

Many of us go through life with numerous health and medical

difficulties and a lot of us come out the other side better than before. Unfortunately, some don't make it and pass on.

I deal with my own internal and external stress by putting pen to paper and I write down my words, thoughts, and quotes. While many of the readers will say that my book may have a few typos, or some incorrect grammar, or thought processes and that I digressed and had too many pictures, quotes, charts, and jokes, I simply say this: I told my story about my experience the best that I could, nothing more and nothing less.

I tried to be as toothful as possible by telling my story and if you liked it feel free to pass it on.

There are always three sides to every story: His, Hers, and the Tooth.

The Tooth will set you free.

We were all created in G-d's image and we have just one life to live, so live it to the Max.

Let's not take ourselves too seriously. None of us has a monopoly on wisdom.

It is said that stories can help put you to sleep; I say that stories can help wake you up.

My granddaughter Maya whom this book is dedicated to has told me many times the following few words: "Papa you will talk to a shoe." I guess I would have to agree, but words can say a lot so, tell your story as I did mine!

Remember to love and cherish all those that are part of your family. Don't forget to kiss the ones you love and love the ones you kiss. Life can change in an instant whether the direction is good or bad.

And finally I would like to conclude with the following few words that say it all:

During the last few years, we have lived through the Covid crisis, the war in Ukraine, inflation being out of control, prices skyrocketing, and politics on both sides of the aisle putting a wedge between us all. But most of us still have our health, our careers, our families, and our social networks to rely on.

Imagine if we all just loved and supported each other for no reason, instead of hating and judging each other for no reason. The world could possibly be a better place for us all.

Imagine that!!!!

May you have peace, happiness, and contentment throughout your journey and keep the faith and a positive attitude and always make some time to monkey around.

And I will conclude with a comment I like to use in the memory of our late son, brother, and friend Max Gold Dwares, who left the world far too early on the eighteenth of February, 2004 at the age of twenty from complications related to his battle with leukemia:

May we all always remember to: **"Live To The Max"**,
Kevin Dwares

And **NO, this is not the author after all of his dental work.**

ACKNOWLEDGEMENTS

I want to thank a family friend of ours, Naomi Lipsky, for all of her time and effort in helping me design and develop the photo on page 71. Her help and guidance were invaluable to me as she helped me to convey my feelings and thoughts over my entire dental journey all through the one photo.

I also want to thank my son, Jake, whose help in the area of computer issues and Excel spreadsheets was invaluable as I began the arduous process of putting the book together. Jake was always eager to help me with technical issues even when I didn't know those issues existed (although they always did). He gave me a great education in the area of saving documents and gave me the great counsel of backing up everything on my computer as well as on an encrypted thumb drive. For all of these items I say thank you, Jake, and let you know that I always have and always will love you and cherish the guidance and advice that you have always given me. And of course I will try not to ask you the same things multiple times as you have always respectfully mentioned to me. You're a great friend, father, husband, and son and should be very proud of yourself for all that you have accomplished.

I also want to thank my daughter-in-law Maria who always lent an open ear whenever I had questions and supplied me with her good humor and friendly banter. Maria is a great mother, wife, daughter-in-law, and friend to all.

I also need to mention my late son Max who passed away at the young age of twenty on February 18, 2004 after battling leukemia for three years. Max had a beautiful smile and great looking teeth and always had a kind word for everyone. He dedicated his short life to helping those in need. May his memory be a blessing.

I also need to thank the love of my life, my wife of forty-two-plus years, Barbara. She stood by me during this process and always offered kind words and understanding even when I drove her crazy at times. I always appreciate her witticisms and constructive criticisms whenever they are presented to me. To be able to have someone to love me during all of our time together whether good or bad is truly a blessing. I can't thank her enough for always standing by my side and I will always cherish her counsel, love, and understanding.

ABOUT THE AUTHOR

Kevin Dwares is a second-time author, writing this book about his dental experiences from June 29, 2020 through October 31, 2022.

Prior to this book, Kevin wrote another entitled *Live to the Max* which was published in 2016 by the Christian Faith Publishing Company. This book was about the life and faith of his late son Max Gold Dwares who passed away on February 18, 2004 at the age of twenty from complications related to a bone marrow transplant to cure him of leukemia.

Prior to writing his first book, Kevin spent over thirty years as a federal employee in the area of contracting and special project management.

During his spare time, he likes to snowshoe in the mountains, exercise, and spend time traveling around the United States and Israel which he has visited nine times. Kevin spends time volunteering at food pantries and collecting donations for local organizations for them to distribute to the needy.

Kevin also volunteers at Rhode Island T.F. Green International Airport as part of a customer-service program that allows members of the community to serve as ambassadors to passengers and visitors. The volunteer program is always in need of more folks. Feel free to reach out. Their website is: https://www.flyri.com/riac/volunteer/.

Kevin also volunteers for the Rhode Island Military Organization located at T.F. Green International Airport. This group supports Rhode Island service members and their families in the military lounge located at the airport. Feel free to reach out to them at: http://RIMilitaryOrganization.com.

Kevin also volunteered at the Tomorrow Fund for children with cancer and has decided to donate all proceeds from the sales of *A Royal Crowning Achievement* to the Tomorrow Fund to help children and their families! Feel free to make a donation to them at:

The Tomorrow Fund
RI Hospital Campus
110 Lockwood Street
Physicians Office Bldg. Suite 422
Providence, RI 02903
(401) 444-8811
www.tomorrowfund.org

Kevin's most important time is spent with his eleven-year-old granddaughter Maya who is named after his late son, Max.

Kevin lives in Cranston, Rhode Island with his wife of forty-two years, Barbara, his dog, Harry, and his cat, Sally. Kevin's son Jake and his wife Maria and their daughter Maya live less than five minutes away so he visits them frequently. Kevin hopes that this new book entitled *A Royal Crowning Achievement* will serve as an inspiration to others who need tremendous amounts of dental work. Although sometimes painful, aggravating and expensive, it is worth taking care of your teeth as they will be with you for many years. Ain't that the Tooth and nothing but the Tooth?